My Heart
Sleeve

Bernadette Brear

BookLeaf
Publishing

Presentation by *BookLeaf Publishing*

Web: www.bookleafpub.com

E-mail: info@bookleafpub.com

ISBN: 9789357617772

First edition 2023

To my husband Nicholas and children AJ and Kayden - without you, my pages would be empty.

To my dearest bestie, Danielle - until we meet again.

ACKNOWLEDGEMENT

To Jeanette for always pushing me to be a better version of myself, you hear me when I speak and encourage the small things I never would think one would take note of (even the hand tattoo). To Mama Michelle for the love & encouragement and putting this out into the universe on my behalf, and for your prayers. To my sister Sam for being my inspiration - I am your biggest fan and to my amazing family for being the better part of my being; Mom (Trudy), Dad (Tony), Fiona - aka Feemo (niece Myah and nephew Connor) and Darren (My Fairy God Child Amelia).

All my friends who I call family - you know who you are and I love you.

PREFACE

I've always written down my feelings, whether it was a song or a poem or even a letter, especially when the going gets tough, but I didn't always share them. My late bestie Danielle always encouraged me to, well and to be a comedian, but let's see how this goes first.

When my eldest went off to college, I wrote "Ode to my Aj" to make them cry (payback for "leaving me"). I added it to my Facebook profile and Mama Michelle (Danielle's mom) contacted me after reading it. She said I could and should put it in a book. My reply was, apart from a giggle, "I wouldn't even know where to start". Well, through some sort of telepathic connection my boss, Jeanette did! Not knowing about my conversation with Michelle at all, Jeanette gave this to me as a gift. I am very blessed and much of a "that is a sign from the universe", so here we are.

Ode to my AJ - You.... and lil old me

You were 2, saying cute things and stuff
"I love you like broccoli" and "we stick together like
cottage pie"
I'd never question you but you'd always tell me why
I was the spicy mince and you were the mash
It was me and you against the world
You and me... that was enough.
(love and kindness)

At 3 you started little school and you learned the
word "no"
You used it a lot, my not-so-favorite was at drop off
the entrance was as far as I was allowed to go
(strength and independence, yes, already!)

At 4 you met a man and chose him before I did
He gave you a bigger family and you gave your
whole heart
from the very start.
There were hard times learning to share me with
more
but life was good,
you were still only 4
(Acceptance)

5 and 6, you were a hippie kid, kind and loving and
pure
You wore two different shoes and loved your messy
hair
Pa was your favorite, I was second best
that you made quite clear
You remained true to you my free and feisty little
bear
you love to hug and cuddle and play, you were
protective of me, a quality at that age, so rare.
(Free yet aware)

Jumping to 7 and also 8, through bullies and brats
causing feelings of hate
You put up a wall and we struggled some more
you became angry in fact
9 and 10 you found yourself a little,
we had the big move and with all feelings brittle
things got hardcore.
(Pain, change, new beginnings)

11 and 12, the hormones kicked in, I thought maybe
by now I'd be slightly prepared but alas I was not
I called my mom apologetically in tears
I didn't know what I was doing as I struggled, I was
scared
(Learning for both of us)

13, 14 you came out to me
I was blazay which made things slightly easy...
well, I had my reservations but it's the 21st century
hey?
You heard me wholeheartedly and accepted my
thoughts, you understood my concerns, accepting I'm
not perfect!
I heard you too as I'd been learning with the new
you,
although you did not know how, when and what to
feel
I felt your feelings, tried to help but failed, you
needed to grow
so I left you to be...
Until you needed me.
And you did, more than once, even when you didn't
know
(Teen, challenges, feeling the darkness)

15 I saw you, you found you even more,
we lost the one person who helped calm us
and our world changed, your heart full of grief.
Everything's different now and so are you, you are
still all the above
in my eyes you're so much more than you believe
(Learning, compassion, dealing with a huge loss)

16 you're leaving, finished with high school and off
to college.

Studying not quite what you've planned but it's pretty close,
You can do what you want because you taught yourself how,
this is your life, your dream, the one you chose
(Bravery)

You did this, we did this, me and you against the world!
Now let's see what the next few years unfold.
We're excited for the unknown and probably still not prepared, but the world is your oyster and your story is still to be told.
I will always be there for you, whenever you need and I thank you for you, my good little seed!
(A good relationship with my child)

Now a little about me, I'm still not ready
Not since you were 3, not then and not now
It's not easy to let you go, be independent, without me by your side.
You have taught me as much as I have taught you and I am bursting with pride,
I hope you are proud of me too.
and on that note I wish you all the best as I cry deep inside
I'm happy for you, and I love you, my child
(A passionate, clingy mom)

Empty Dreams

The one that got away...

In the time I spent with you and everything we
shared
I did not know what it was although nothing
could compare
You kept a soul believed to be unwanted and
gave it back so pure
To my hurtful sickness only you were my cure
Because we could not be that time, due to
circumstance
I'd have you know that if I could, I'd give a
second chance

Every time I close my eyes I see you standing
there
But when I try to reach for you, you just
disappear
I would do things differently
Acceptance being the key
If only I could have you here
And not just in my empty dreams

Magnetic Voice

Being away from the one that calms you...

Everything is a blur and chaos starts to rise
Nothing seems to make much sense
There's no Bonny without her Clyde
When darkness becomes blinding
And silence becomes deafening
Your voice is the only thing that I'll try to find
Like static electricity
Calm rushes through me
My emotions pulled to bind
That magnetic voice
Too strong to part
My soul is yours,
And only with you
Belongs my fragile heart

*That first love is always exciting and you learn
quite a lot of what you want and don't want in a
relationship. Don't lose hope, you've got this.

The Interview

One of the worst interviews in the world (True
Story - Company Name Omitted)

An interview I went to once, at... let's say, an
interior decorating company
What a horrible woman she was
when she insulted me

2 days ago, she had called to arrange a time
I said to her "I dress like a fairy and my hair is
dreaded, is that fine?"
She said to me "no problem at all, that we can
work around"
"I like you very much you see, we clicked the
minute you took my call"

She proceeds to tell me all about her divorce and
her very sad life
and after arranging a date and time she said to
me
"The job is practically yours and I look forward
to seeing you at 5"
I arrived there early and prepared, I had to wait
because she was not there

The first lady I greeted, slightly heavier than me
was wearing sneakers and jeans
The skinny dude, dressed the same and making a
cup of tea,
under his breath snickered and giggled at me
when the boss arrived, he handed her the tea and
said "this you are going to need"

In a long purple skirt, a pretty black top and
beads around my wrists
I sat there in a total blank listening to her ugly
words

"You dress in too much colour, your skin is not
so nice"
"You're overweight, your hair is bad, you're not
thinking straight"
"I can't have you here for my customers to see"
"Oh imagine how embarrassing that will be"
"You stupid girl, What are you thinking being
this person you are"
"You have to change and very quick, if you want
to get far"

At the end, when she was done, I said "thank
you for being so honest"
and walked away clutching my fists
thinking
how my personality she tried to rob

but failed, because
I AM STRONG

* I have been blessed with 2 auto-immune
diseases, Alopecia and Vitiligo and have lived
with it since I was 18 years old and at the time
of this interview, I had just had my second child.

** Don't allow other people's words get to you,
no one defines you, YOU DO and ONLY YOU.
Listen to Christina Aguilera's song - Beautiful

Words Kill

Abuse/Bullying in any way, shape or form is so
dangerous and could lead to suicide!
To the few we have lost on the way, we hope
you found peace.

Tears falling down her face,
Soul and mind totally bleak
she's trapped inside her head
She has forgotten how to speak
Her true feelings she can never share
Her smile hiding an unnoticeable pretending
The constant bullying is just too much to bare

The things they said were not meant to be sound
They pushed and pushed until she broke down
They did not care or feel or see
Seeing her broken was too funny

What could she do to feel again?
What had she tried before?
The scars on her wrists show previous pain,
a feeling she needed to rid

She went to her drawer, fell to the floor
Feeling free and she smiled

She knew, this, what she had done
was not the right thing to do
but the darkness was fading
and the pain would never again face
One last laugh
One last sigh
Emotions run dry
Gone
To her own happy place

* But what happens to those who pushed her to
that point?
We need to do better, look deeper and feel softer.
Be conscious of what you say and how you say
it.

Metaphor of Love (all the senses in one)

I was 19 when I met my husband, and sometimes,
just sometimes I still feel this way when he is around
me...

Like the most intense sight you see, an invigorating
smell
touching the most exquisite silk, tasting the indulgent
cake
the feeling.... awe!

I dance in my profound thoughts to the sounds of my
heart's beats
The addiction these senses have to those
to have it all the time
I have the same when you are close
my senses dance and heart becomes a chime

Losing you is a fear
The only thought I have is you
You are the only dream I feel
I am senseless when you are not here

*Co-dependency is not good for you but being in a
relationship where someone adores you and will do
anything for you, is nice. Remember, what you also
put in you get out.

A teenage crush

You know when you are young and you have
that 1 crush on someone who is close to you and
fear of saying anything takes over and then they
introduce their new adored to you? yes? me too,
been there, done that, totally made it rhyme :)

I see your smile almost every day
and hide the way I feel
I want to tell you everything
but my lips are sealed
I think I love you with all my heart
but you will never know
I have to lock those feelings away
yet I hope they never go

Now you are here and so is she
you are hand in hand
Oh I can't stand it, I hate to see
how beautiful you two look
while my heart suffers in silence
because of a chance I never took

* take chances and make changes and mistakes
but always align it with you first and what
makes you happy!

Poison Arrow

That toxic relationship break-up, the angry phase
and when everything is overly dramatic!

Extreme seduce of love and light brought but
darkness
blurred my sight
took my soul hidden deep divine
you're no angel of mine
taken back
worthy you're not
a poison arrow in my heart you shot
as the pain slowly goes away
The purest love will find me again.

* write - I encourage you to write down
everything you feel in a blog or story or journal
or poem - don't bottle your feelings.

An Angel called SAM

At 18, I moved out to be on my own. I was in a very
toxic relationship and was hurting myself. I was also
very depressed. My big sister noticed something was
wrong and went out of her way to get me help - I
thought I was hiding my pain, but those who love you
can see right through your darkness.

I am alone. I can't even cry.
I cannot feel. I'm dying inside.
Holding on with all my might to a burning candle
The cold wind blows across my face.
The candle dies, returning to the dark place.
The sight is vague, but a soft voice I can hear
calling me, coming near.
The voice is now closer; this voice is not new.
Grabbing my arm and pulling me through
and in the light.
I see you.
Thank you for seeing me when I look away.
Thank you for leading me when I am astray
Thank you, just thank you.
When my world is a sham,
You really are my angel. Sam

*We just need to accept the help.

Facetime with Feemo

I moved to the UK, following my husband and left my entire world in South Africa, Feemo (Fiona), who should have been my twin, and I have always been really close and it's not at all easy being so far away from your family.

Facetime with Feemo
Cannot be without vodka or wine
We speak about everything for a long period of time
Complain about the children from biggest to small
We sip and we giggle and we sip some more
While her face on my phone goes wherever I go
We'll be interrupted by children well, you know...
from their gross toilet habits, the screaming and shouting
This one is pushing and that one is pouting
The husband trying to get his 2 cents worth in
The pots over boiling or the chips overcooking
the overloaded washing machine has moved itself to the door on its spin
At this point we were trying to find a quiet place to hide in.

Our conversations do go many different ways
The deep ones, the honest, even encouragement
and praise
There's one thing not lacking not one single day
How much we love and miss each other
and wish so hard we can be together again.

*Everyone needs a sister like Fee, who tells it
like it is and is very protective. If you don't have
a real one, I'm sure you have a friend that is
practically one.

Mom

My mom is one of the greatest women you could ever know. I adore her with every part of my being and I am so lucky to have her. This is part of a song I wrote for her in my very younger days. I think I played it for her on mother's day (with my guitar)

For 9 months you carried me in your womb
You brought me into this world
You gave me my name, held me close to your heart
And in my life, played the biggest part
I can tell you why I'm the luckiest girl in the world
You're the perfect mom for a girl
When I'm hurt, you fix me up with your words
You encourage me with your smile
Spending time with you is always worthwhile

You are an angel sent from above
You show me the good and bad things through life
You protect me and teach me and love me
You know where you stand
I might not say it mom but I'm your biggest fan

You're an inspiration to everyone around
You're always there
So are the good times we shared
I'll never forget you're my pillar of strength
My wisdom and my guide
Now that I'm older and you're still here to see
How my beautiful mother has grown within me

* My momsie is hardcore, loving, encouraging,
accepting and so very honest. One of a kind -
there's no lesson here besides me learning from
her.

What a woman

My Sam, again. Sam worked next door to me,
I'd spend my lunch times with her every day.
She moved away and I took over her job, after
she got married, I wrote this poem. I think I was
about 23 years old. Lol, good times

Who would have thought
That a word so short
Could have a huge meaning
To us all...
Sammy, a song I find hard to write
But a poem I have done
For you, is this one

I look back at the days
The silly things we have done
Two little children having some fun
To have Sam as a sister
Is truly exciting
I couldn't have asked
For any better

She watched me grow and I watched her
I did what she did, dressed like her too
I copied her and followed her around,

like little sisters do.
We played the weirdest games
Like *Under the bed???
Hence the little dents in our heads

We sang funny songs
Threw mud at trees and
Together we would terrorise Fee
We'd go out into space from our closets
To visit our fairies and hobbits

She walks with her head held up high
Her talented hand writes funny poems
Her graceful nature and word only wise
She is strong and graceful.

Now we are grown
She's a woman of note
SAMMY FOR PRESIDENT
(she'd get my first vote)

She married a man like her he is
Kinda puts my mind at ease
She's worked so hard
And waited so long
Lived her life
And now she's a perfect wife
One day, married I'll be
I still really hope, like her I can be

WHAT A WOMAN

* Under-the-bed is a game where 1 of us would go under the bed and the remaining 2 sisters would be on top. We would then drop our heads to look at the 1 under the bed who would then have to try to slap you with a shoe. If you were struck, you had to replace the person under the bed.
Please note that none of us are aggressive, my parents probably would have stopped us playing the game had any of us complained, and we were little. My siblings and I are very close to this day. Good to be born in the '80s.

His song

In my very younger days, I was obsessed with
Ash and his music. We spent a lot of time
playing guitar and chilling. We are sadly no
longer in touch but I hope he still plays...

He wonders what his next word should be
About her, that sad memory
He's broken yet calm and stuck in this place
Cursed by a girl, so untame
One man's sorrow
another's game

He sings of the rain, the moon and the stars
Of the people around him and his broken heart
His voice so powerful when he sings his song
And the anger shows as he plays the guitar
To him it's personal, yet I know what he means
What's he's feeling, I'm feeling,
the internal screams

For hours
I could listen to him play his beautiful song
He has the voice of an angel, I wish he could
see, the voice of an angel,
Dearest Ashley

The tears fall when I hear his words
I feel it when he sings, when he sings his hurt
If only I could take those feelings away
Make him feel what I feel when he sings, when
he plays
The more I listen
The more the world should hear
This boy, I hold close to my heart, so dear

For hours I could watch him play his guitar
And list to him sing his beautiful song
He has the voice of an angel
I wish he could see
The voice of an angel
My dear friend, Ashley.

April 2009

No one like you

A li'l happy Bornday to my big sis!

From small to big and near to far
I can always count on you
in happy times to losing my hair
you always seem to be there
from silly games and tag team boxing
I remember inventing with you
to high school missions and finding new friends
our bond remained true
I followed you, every step
from waitressing (at the same place)
to bookkeeping, and now...
no, I can't bake
So I think bookkeeping's where I'll stay
What I am actually trying to say
is I think you're fantabulistigorrificaly amazing
and a great role model, perhaps to a few
and there will never be
a better big sister than you

April 2019

Just for you

(a song, no poem) For my husband who never
gives up on me, loves me in all ways and
proposed to me when I was flu infested,
wrapped up in a blanky and struggling to find
the will to live (slightly dramatic, I know)

My mind has been a wreck
Time has moved so slow
but love has been so kind to me
Which makes it easier to know that
I really do see that
You are always there for me
you push me to be better
and that is why
This poem is just for you
I was too scared to get close
scared of getting hurt
you took that fear away
thank you is all I can say
I gave you my heart
while it was torn
you mended it and kept it warm
you brought happiness to my life
I have fallen in love
and I love being your wife

I want to you to know that
I love you more now than ever before
And I will do anything to prove it to you
From the bottom of my heart
Nothing can tear us apart
You are always there for me
you understand me better than I do
and that is why
This poem is just for you

* Nicholas Brear, I truly love you with all of my being.

Mother & Kitten

This one is sad, I witnessed the heartbreak of a
mommy losing her newly born kitten.

she lies there still
as cold as the night
sick and tired of fighting for life
her caring mother does not know
that to heaven she had to go

so she cleans her and holds her
to keep her warm
and lies there waiting
for her to feed and squirm
then we take Rolly away

for hours & hours she calls her one
but she's gone to the corner
buried
under the sun

mom lies there
waiting for her baby to come
her green eyes are teary
she lets out a sigh
she does not know

how to say
goodbye

she lies there
doing nothing for days
but knows deep down
it's mother nature's ways

RIP Rolly (our newborn grey kitty)

The Garden

your thoughts, the seeds
the seed, your fear
self-destruction
actions, reactions
the see, that weed, you do not hear

Sub-conscious mind
THE CONTROLLED
the nightmares, your beliefs
words, pictures, insults

conscious mind
THE CONTROLLER
the GARDENER
feelings, intuition, choice
sowing unwanted thoughts and feelings

the flowers
weeds - negativity
black, dry, wild, ugly
you are ugly
your garden is ugly - depression
the mind now corrupt
my mind
my garden

uncontrollable weeds
growing deep into my soul
suffocating me
tearing me apart
the feelings, the thoughts
depression
PAINFUL DEPRESSION
that seeded
MY GARDEN

YOU
another seed
my child
your mind is now my mind
willpower
mindpower

you saved me.

I wrote this poem whilst pregnant and single. I
had given into the darkness and through the
want to be a good mom, I made some drastic
changes and I continue to keep my garden clean
from weeds that may try to sneak in.
26/07/2006

My KP

As I sit trying to find the correct words
To explain this beautiful soul
All I find myself doing is giggling
She is me, in a nutshell

So gentle, so kind, does not (yet) break rules
Happy and chatty telling stupid jokes to name a
few
She will make you laugh, and convince you to
dance
You will want to be around her whenever you
have the chance

She's graceful, a queen and knows what she
wants
And stubborn but not nasty and can put up a
front
She does not take nonsense
but when confronted
She may shut down

But when she strongly disagrees
With whatever you say or do
Our adorable little ballerina
Goes KP KABOOM

This poem is referenced from a show we used to watch called Katie Ka-boom on Animaniacs. Kayden is not a reactive but at the right moment we will joke with her that this is who she reminds us of. Teehee
This poem has been proofread and approved by K.P (to avoid the kaboom)

My Bestie

We moved to this house in somer-strand
It's number 193
Next door lived a boy and girl with their family
Ian, maybe 5 popped his head over the wall
cricket was on the play
We invited him over, he said he had a sister
But when we called her, she'd run away.
Mom and Pops would go out on Mondays
And I was asked to go sit
Danielle believed me sitting was stupid
Well, we were of similar age
It was more of a number thing anyway and
probably about her brother
This went on for a while and although situations
changed
We always stayed close and grew up together
From little girls, to dramatic teens, to working
adults and moms
In the meantime, we said goodbye to Ian
He left us dramatically, he left the biggest hole
In the heart of my Dandy.
As we worked with the pain and continued
through life
Many dramas and mistakes were made
Dandy worked hard to change her life

And managed to laugh again.
Although we've fought and we've screamed
and ignored each other for days
we've also cried and rescued each other from
worst ways
Our children know us to be crazy
We were fun and also strict
Distance became the biggest issue between us
But nothing stopped us from calling
My bestie's face on all our phones every single
day
We spoke and we studied and we filled our
nights
With all the happenings of the days
even tea parties with Tillie and singsongs galore
Until one day the dreadful call
That her voice will be no more
Dandy left us all
My heart sank and it still does to this day
This is a feeling that will never go away.
She leaves behind Thalia, her legacy.
We are all missing her dearly
She's etched deep in our hearts
And I will never forget her
My bestie, our Dandy-lion.
Our forever. ♥

Heart on my sleeve

No matter how hard I try
Not to take things personally
My brain, my soul and my heart
Work very differently
I feel what you feel
And cry when you do
And I'll feel your rage
Even when I don't want to

I'll love everyone hugely
And I'll be very loyal
And if anyone's upset with me
My whole body's in turmoil
I am kind and I'm strong
And I work really hard
I'm brave and quite funny
I try not to do wrong

The times that I mess up
I struggle more with me
I overthink and feel everything
But you'll never see
I may be sensitive or emotional
But there's little I'll show
Unless you are close to me

Being an empath is hard
Although sometimes a gift
Some people I have to withdraw from
And some people I like keep
I also need to protect me
Because
I wear my heart on my sleeve

Ingram Content Group UK Ltd.
Milton Keynes UK
UKHW020235210623
423745UK00015B/464

COOKING THE BOOKS

APPLE ORCHARD COZY MYSTERY BOOK 2

CHELSEA THOMAS

Big +
LITTLE
PRESS

Want updates, free cozies and recipes? Join the Chelsea Thomas Reader Club at chelseathomasauthor.com.

Cover Design, Priscilla Pantin

Edited by, Marjorie Kramer

 Created with Vellum

To our friends

DOLLARS AND DECEPTION

*N*othing ruins a quaint, small-town festival like finding a frozen corpse during the sled race.

That's a lesson I learned firsthand at Pine Grove's Winter Festival when I found a frozen corpse during the sled race.

But I'd had a bad feeling in my bones for days before that.

It started when my aunt, Miss May, met with her accountant to go over her finances.

The meeting took place in the bakeshop on the orchard Miss May owned. Although the bakeshop was rustic and cozy and filled with smells of cinnamon sugar and apples, on that day the place had a dreary energy.

I blamed the accountant.

Charles Fitz, CPA, was in his late 50s. He had slicked back hair, and perfect teeth, and a big-city vibe that was out of place in our small town of Pine Grove, New York.

I tried to keep a polite distance as Miss May and Charles talked. But they were having their meeting at one of the tables in the bakeshop. And I had to prep four hundred of

Miss May's famous Appie Oater cookies for the next day. So I couldn't help but listen in on the heated conversation.

Miss May leaned forward with her hands balled on the table. "What do you mean I can't take my money out!?"

Charles sat back, with a hint of a smile on his face. "Now, now, I never said you can't take it out. I said that as your wealth manager, I recommend that you keep your money in the fund."

"It's not wealth you're managing," Miss May said. "It's working capital! I need it for repairs, and payroll, and—"

"Sure," Charles said, hands in the air. "Repairs, payroll, that stuff costs money. You know I get that, May. All I'm saying is I expect big returns. Soon. You'd be a fool to exit the fund now."

"So how long do you need?"

Charles took a deep breath and locked his fingers behind his combed-back hair. His wrist watch reflected the light above the table. "Two weeks. A month. Tops."

Miss May shook her head. "That doesn't work for me, Charles. Now, I understand your job is to make me money, but—"

"My job is to make you rich."

"I'll get rich when I'm dead. For now I just need to keep the bills paid."

"Isn't the expression 'I'll rest when I'm dead?'" Charles asked.

"I'll never get rich if I rest," Miss May said. "So when can I expect the money transferred back into my account?"

Charles sighed and sat up straight, taking a more serious tone. "You want the whole sum?"

"That's right," Miss May said.

"Can I convince you to keep half with me? I'm telling

you. This is a solid investment. You'll double your money in no time."

"What type of investment is it?" Miss May asked.

I watched Charles as I placed big balls of cookie dough onto the baking sheet. The way he shifted in his chair made me uncomfortable.

"I can't disclose that information," Charles said. "But trust me. This opportunity is once in a lifetime."

Miss May rubbed her chin, considering the proposal. "I guess I could keep half with you. At least for now."

"How about three-quarters?" Charles didn't miss a beat.

"I don't know," Miss May said. "I need to put some of that money back into the farm."

Charles smiled. "You have to take big risks to get big rewards, May. Imagine the improvements you could make with increased capital."

Miss May bit her lip. She hated the possibility of missing out on a big opportunity, and Charles was saying all the right things to convince her to take the risk.

"It would be nice to double my money," she said. "Perhaps you're right. It might be smart to keep at least part of the money in your fund."

"Just part?" Charles leaned in, and the greedy look in his eyes hit me right in the stomach.

"Wait!" I said.

Both Miss May and Charles turned.

"I think you should take your money out," I said to Miss May. "Every penny!"

Fitz scoffed. "That's ridiculous! She just said she wants to leave the money with me!"

Miss May looked over at me. "Why do you say that, Chelsea?"

Uhhhhhh...

I hadn't prepared a statement. But it was too late to back out, so I babbled, as I often did. "I mean, I'm no expert, but I have a friend in finance. In the city. They've been telling me the market's supposed to crash. Soon. So... yeah. Not a good time for risky investments."

"What's your friend's name?" Charles asked. "I know tons of guys in finance."

"It's a woman, as a matter of fact." No reason my lie couldn't be empowering to women.

"Well, she's wrong," Charles said.

"I doubt it," I said. "Her name is...Millini Gustafo. She's the youngest woman to ever work as a VP at one of the Big Five. You can search her on your phone."

Big five!? Search her on your phone? What was I doing?

"That's a great idea," Charles pulled out his smart phone. "How do you spell Millini? Never heard that one."

He had a good point. Millini was the fakest name in the history of fake names. "Uh. She's French. And Filipina. And Chinese! A quarter, on her mother's side."

"French-Filipina-Chinese. Exotic." Charles opened the browser on his phone. "How do you spell the name?"

I stammered. "Uh— Uh— Starts with an M..."

Charles laughed and spat his next words like venom. "That's what I figured. 'Uh uh uh!' Stupid, fake, made-up name. Why are you trying to sabotage me, Chelsea? Are you that bored? Don't you have any more cookies to bake?"

"Charles!" Miss May stood.

Charles gasped as though he had shocked himself along with us. "Oh my goodness! I'm so sorry. That came from nowhere. Chelsea. Please forgive me. I should not have snapped. It's just, the name sounded, uh, I'm sorry. There's no excuse."

"Too late, Fitz." Miss May looked Charles square in the eye. "I want my money back. All of it."

Charles tittered. "May! Don't let my small lapse in social etiquette sway you. This opportunity is once in a lifetime. I don't want you to miss out."

"I've missed out on plenty in my life," Miss May said. "I don't need to be rich to be happy."

Charles laughed. "Everyone needs to be rich, May. Are you crazy?"

"Sure, Charles. I'm crazy. Can you transfer the money this evening?"

Charles sighed. "All of it? You're certain?"

Miss May crossed her arms. "Yep."

"Are you sure I can't—"

"Charles!"

"OK, OK." Charles said. He looked at me. "Millini Gustafo, huh?"

I nodded.

"She must know something I don't."

I shrugged. *Guess so, ya creep!*

"Charles," Miss May said. "Are you going to transfer the money?"

"Yeah, yeah," Charles said. "I'll make the withdrawal request. You should have your investment back in three to five business days."

"Too long," Miss May said. "I want the money tonight."

"The government regulates large withdrawals," Charles said. "It takes time."

Miss May narrowed her eyes. Charles shrugged. It looked like he was telling the truth.

"Fine," Miss May said. "I'll give you the week."

Charles let out a deep exhale. "And I can't convince you to leave something in?"

"No, you cannot," Miss May said.

"OK. Thank you for your business." Charles stood up, smoothed his rumpled suit, and headed out of the kitchen.

He turned back before he left. "Those cookies smell incredible, by the way."

I smiled. "They'll be on sale all week in the bake shop."

Charles nodded and exited.

Miss May and I froze to listen as he left the house. The heels of his dress shoes clacked on the wood floors. Then the front door creaked open and closed with a thud. And he was gone.

I breathed a sigh of relief as Charles drove his car off the farm. But when I turned back to Miss May her face was ghost-white, and she had furrowed her eyebrows so deep they almost touched.

"Miss May. What's wrong?"

Miss May looked down, squeezed her eyes shut and rubbed the bridge of her nose.

"What is it?" I asked again.

Miss May looked up, and her face was even whiter. Her voice trembled as she spoke.

"That man has all my money."

Later that day, we went to *Grandma's* to eat lunch with Teeny in our favorite booth.

Miss May told Teeny the story of what had happened with Charles, and Teeny couldn't believe her tiny little ears.

"What do you mean Charles has all your money?" Teeny's eyes bugged out. "Like half?"

"No, T," Miss May said. "I mean the majority. Ninety percent."

"You're the smartest woman I know," Teeny said. "Why would you invest with that kid? He stinks like a rat from a mile away!"

"I didn't give the money to Charles. I gave it to his dad. Before..."

"Before he lost his marbles in the loony hole?"

Miss May nodded. "I wouldn't put it like that. But yes. I trusted Old Bill."

"Now his sneaky kid's trying to screw you!" Teeny was getting all worked up, and I didn't like it.

"Can you two please try to relax?" I put my hand on Miss May's arm. "You told Charles you want your money back. Everything will be fine."

"Now you say that," Miss May said. "Two hours ago you were inventing exotic friends to give me a reason to pull my cash."

"That was because I didn't trust his 'secret' investment. But we've got no reason to believe he'll run off with your cash. He's let you make withdrawals before, right?"

Miss May nodded. "And he always processes them on time."

"And you said you got an email from the bank, right? About the withdrawal being initiated?"

Miss May nodded once more.

I threw up my hands in exasperation. "So why are we all so worried?"

A burly voice boomed from behind me. "Charles Fitz is trying to steal everybody's money!"

We turned to see the town lawyer, Tom Gigley, approaching in a huff. He hitched up his pants and sat beside Teeny in the booth.

"What are you talking about?" Miss May said.

"What do you think I'm talking about?" Gigley said. "That little weasel won't let me make a withdrawal!"

Miss May, Teeny, and I gasped, but Gigley was too busy flagging a passing waiter to register our shock. "Yeah, can I get two slices of Boston Cream and a chocolate chip cookie?"

"Back it up, Gigley! What did you say?" Teeny leaned in, eyes wide.

"You heard me. The little creep's taken my money hostage."

"How much?" Teeny pressed her palms into the table.

"All of it! I invested every nickel and dime and Sacajawea with his old man years ago!" Gigley looked down and shuffled his silverware. "Shame what's happened with Bill."

"It sure is," Miss May said. "But that doesn't make it OK for his kid to steal our money."

"You have got to be kidding me," Gigley said. "He's got your money too?"

Miss May stirred her coffee. "He said I could get it back, but it'd take a few days."

"Same thing he told me," said Gigley.

"So maybe it's true," I said. "Right?"

Miss May shrugged. Gigley sipped his coffee. Neither of them seemed optimistic, and we all settled into a contemplative funk.

Then a quiet ding-ding brought me back to the present.

I checked my phone. I had a text message from an unknown number...

"PINE GROVE DAM. 7 PM. IT'S ABOUT THE CASH."

"Whoa," I said. I reached over to show Miss May my phone, but then her phone dinged.

Then Gigley's phone dinged, and I could tell by his

slack-jawed expression that he had just received the same message.

"Dam?" I said.

Gigley nodded. "7 p.m."

I took a deep breath and let it out with a puff.

I didn't particularly feel like going to the Pine Grove Dam, partly because it was freezing outside and partly for more, well, personal reasons. Dread gurgled in my stomach.

"That's kind of late," said Teeny.

"Kind of late" was an understatement. Seven o'clock might as well have been midnight in Pine Grove, so whatever was going on... it was serious.

2

MIDNIGHT MARAUDERS

*T*he Pine Grove Dam was like our little Niagara Falls. Deep, churning water at the top of a reinforced wall. A waterfall cascading to a small holding pool. And a quaint little park off to the side with big maple trees, picnic benches, and a trailhead leading up into the woods.

When the town constructed the Pine Grove Dam in 1830, it was the largest dam in the world. The governor had built the dam to meet the rising demands for water in New York City, and it still served that purpose. But in modern times, the dam was more famous for its leisurely park atmosphere than its water supply.

In the warmer months, the dam was a popular spot for families, hikers, and picnickers to spend a lazy afternoon. And it was a famous proposal spot for happy couples. Or, in my case, not-so-happy couples.

Ugh, so here we go...

My ex-fiancé, Mike, had proposed to me at the dam several years prior. We had been in town for Miss May's birthday, but he had insisted on taking me on a "quick picnic" at the dam before we went to the party. I had been sweaty and grumpy for the entire outing. Until Mike had gotten down on one knee and uttered those timeless words: "Chelsea, you want to be my wife or whatever?"

At the sight of Mike kneeling there, my mind had blanked. Then I'd agreed to marry him, without a second thought. Or a first thought, really. *What's that they say about hindsight? It's better than foresight or something.*

Yeah. Being left at the altar had not only ruined my relationship with Mike, it had ruined my relationship with the Pine Grove Dam. So as we approached that night, I white-knuckled my door handle like I was about to go over the falls in a barrel.

Miss May glanced over at me. "You OK?"

I nodded. We were already at the dam. *What choice did I have?*

As we pulled into the parking lot at the foot of the dam, I realized I had never been there in the winter. Let me tell you, the place was spooky. The limbs on the bare trees looked like skeleton fingers clawing at the sky. The waterfall rumbled and crashed in the darkness. And a thin layer of ice-crusted snow covered the entire park.

We arrived at the dam fifteen minutes early to prep hot chocolate in the kitchenette for whoever else might show up, but there were already a dozen people gathered around a picnic table when we pulled in.

As soon as we parked and got out of the big yellow VW bus, Brian, the owner of the local coffee spot, walked over to meet us. Even under such stressful circumstances, Brian had a serene, SoCal vibe that put me at ease.

"Miss May. Chels. Hey."

Miss May greeted Brian with a hug. "Any idea what's going on?"

"Nah. Not yet." Brian rubbed his hands together to keep them warm.

"How about the text?" I said. "Any word on who sent it?"

Brian broke into his wide, California smile. "Look at you two. Barely rested after solving the biggest case in Pine Grove history, and you're already working a new mystery."

Miss May and I exchanged a look. *We weren't doing that... were we?*

"We just want to figure out what's going on," Miss May said. "Like everybody else."

"Whatever you say, Sherlock." Brian chuckled. "Hey, I brought hot cocoa from the shop if you two want some."

"We brought hot cocoa from our shop!" I said.

"Stiff competition," Brian said. "Maybe we should conduct a blind taste test. Loser buys the winner an ad in next week's paper. 'Best Cocoa for a Creepy Meet-Up.'"

"Your hot chocolate's obviously better than mine," Miss May said. "But if you'd like to go toe-to-toe on baked goods, you're on."

"I buy my baked goods from you!" Brian shook his head in good-natured disbelief, but his smile faded. "So you guys think this is about that slime-ball Fitz?"

"He's got your money too?" Miss May looked concerned.

As Brian and Miss May chatted, I craned my neck to see who else was over by the picnic table. Gigley was there. So was Sudeer, and a few other small business owners from town.

"Everyone's over there, huh?" I asked.

Brian nodded. "Yep. But I'm not sure what we're supposed to do if whoever sent that text doesn't show their face."

Miss May pointed out toward the woods: "That may be them now."

I looked over and saw a hooded figure approaching from the darkness, using a small flashlight to guide the way.

I took a few steps back toward the van, ready to flee if things turned ugly. But Miss May walked right out to meet the figure.

"Miss May!" I called after her. But she kept walking out into the field, so I trotted past the picnic table to catch up. The others followed a few steps behind me. And three seconds later, we were all standing mere feet from the mysterious Pine Grove Texter.

Miss May addressed the hooded figure without a trace of fear in her voice. "Who are you?"

The hooded figure just stood there.

"Did you send that text?" Miss May's voice was sharp, purposeful. Again, the hooded figure did not respond. Miss May continued, annoyed. "Oh, come on. I can't be here all night. If you're not going to—"

The figure held up a leather-gloved hand to halt Miss May, then... it spoke.

"Welcome, all. Thank you for coming. I have a great deal to tell you. But before we begin, I must collect all cell phones, tablets, and other mobile devices."

Miss May laughed. "Seriously!? It's you?"

"Who's you?" I asked.

The figure removed its hood, and the crowd erupted with whispers.

It was Liz, the editor — and only reporter — from the Pine Grove Gazette.

Miss May shook her head, "Nice entrance, Liz. Dramatic,"

"This is a dramatic situation," Liz said. "Now. Make with the mobile devices."

Gigley turned away from Liz to shield her from his phone. "I don't like this. Why do you need our phones?"

"Because," Liz said. "You can never be too careful."

"I'm keeping mine," Gigley said.

"That's fine," Liz said. "I hereby adjourn this meeting."

Liz turned and walked back toward the forest. Miss May turned to Gigley. "Tom, it's Liz. Humor her."

"It's the principle of the matter," Gigley said.

"Gimme the darn phone," Miss May snatched Gigley's phone and called out to Liz. "Yoo-hoo! Got his phone! We're all good!"

Liz turned back. "Are there any others who have an issue with my methodologies?"

No one spoke up, so Liz opened her purse and walked from person to person, nodding as they dropped their phones into her bag. Once Liz had all the phones, she reclaimed her spot at the head of the group.

"I have gathered you all here today, because I suspect Charles Fitz...has swindled you."

"We knew that!" Gigley said. "Fitz got every business owner in town."

Brian and Miss May grumbled in agreement. Within a few seconds the whole group was arguing loudly about what to do.

I could see that things were erupting into total chaos, so I decided to be proactive.

"Guys, let's try to listen to Liz!" I shouted, but no one so much as looked in my direction. I tried again. "Quiet down, everyone! Liz has something to say!"

Miss May climbed onto the picnic table and stomped her big, booted foot. "Shut your apple pie holes, people!"

Everyone stopped talking and Miss May gestured toward me, calm as could be. "Chels, you have something to say?"

I froze. "Oh. So. Um, I was wondering... If everyone might want to perhaps listen to Liz? She could have helpful information."

"Thank you, Chelsea," Liz said. "I'm glad someone here appreciates my investigative leg-work."

Miss May sighed. "Get down to business, Liz."

"OK." Liz cleared her throat and smoothed her jacket. "As I'm sure you are all aware, Charles Fitz is managing a large sum of money for every person gathered here. Further, each of us has requested a withdrawal, which Charles has refused or delayed the process. Thus, I suspect that Charles has spent our money, or worse, lost it in a risky investment. And I've gathered everyone here this evening to discuss a course of action."

"What's the course of action?" I asked.

"I don't have one," Liz said. "That's what I want to discuss."

"You don't have a plan?" Gigley said. "Then why are we here?"

Liz shrugged. "A clandestine meeting seemed appropriate. Isn't this how scandals work?"

Sudeer stepped forward. "The first step usually involves contacting the authorities. Have you been in touch with the cops or the FBI?"

A voice boomed from the darkness behind us. "There's no need."

I turned toward the sound, and there was Detective Wayne Hudson, stepping out from behind a tree. With his broad shoulders and confident swagger, he looked like a cowboy. Except for the fact that he was hiding behind a tree, which was not cowboy-like at all.

I couldn't help but take a good-natured jab. "Wayne. Were you hiding behind a tree?"

"I was conducting surveillance on Liz," Wayne turned to Liz. "Last week, Charles Fitz filed a complaint that you've been stalking him."

"That's ridiculous," Liz said. "I just happened to be in the same places as him, on several occasions, every day."

"It's fine," Wayne said. "He didn't press charges. But he did express concern that you might be spreading rumors about him and his business."

"What rumors?" Miss May asked. "Everything Liz said is true."

"Sure," Wayne said. "Except the part where Charles lost everyone's money."

"He still has the cash?" Brian asked.

Wayne nodded.

"How can you be sure?" Liz asked. "Everyone here is waiting on a withdrawal."

"Officer Flanagan and I have been watching Fitz since long before you have," Wayne said to Liz. "We brought him into the station last week, and he gave us full access to his accounts. Turns out he's had a dozen withdrawal requests in the last week alone. Everyone overreacting to volatility in the market. He needs time to process the requests. That's all."

"Or he's thinking about skipping town with everyone's money," Gigley said. "Isn't that what these 'wealth managers' do?"

"He can't skip town," Wayne said. "We've got him flagged in the system. If he so much as pays a toll on the way out of Pine Grove, we'll bring him into the station for questioning."

Liz stepped forward. "I think you're on his payroll! Charles told you to come here and lie to us, didn't he?"

"He did not," Wayne said. "And I've more than proven my commitment to this town."

"Eh," Miss May said, ribbing Wayne. My aunt and I had played an integral role in solving Pine Grove's last big crime, and Miss May wasn't about to give Detective Hudson all the credit.

Liz wasn't ready to back down either.

"I don't buy it," Liz said. "I detect corruption, manipulation, deceit, and lies! And I will not rest until—"

Liz's phone buzzed. "Until..."

Her phone buzzed again. She checked it and her face dropped. "Oh."

"What happened?" Gigley said.

Liz looked down. "I uh... I got my transfer from Charles. My withdrawal request came through."

"All of it?" Gigley asked.

Liz nodded. "Every penny."

"So the cop is right," Gigley said. "Next time you host a secret rendezvous, can we do it someplace warm?"

Liz nodded and kicked at the snow, like a child caught misbehaving. "Sorry, everyone."

"It's fine," Miss May rubbed Liz's back. "We appreciate all you do for us. And for this town. Right, gang?"

"That's right," Brian said. "But man, am I happy you were wrong!"

The group laughed in relief, but as I looked from face to smiling face... I couldn't shake an uneasy feeling.

As Detective Hudson turned to leave, I followed him out to the parking lot. I was on the hunt for more information.

Wayne didn't look up as he unlocked his car. "Are you following me?"

"Don't flatter yourself, Officer." I surprised myself with my sass.

"Detective," Wayne said as he turned to me. "So what were you doing?"

"I guess... I was following you." I hung my head.

Wayne grinned. "Well, I'm not going back to hide in the trees, if that's what you're hoping."

I grinned right back. "Why would I hope that?"

Wayne shrugged. "No reason."

Wayne seemed relaxed as he leaned on his unmarked cruiser, but my insides were in full-on panic mode. *Was this flirting?* I had no idea. But Wayne was looking at me like it was my turn to talk. *Oh right. It was my turn to talk!*

"Actually. I wanted to talk to you," I said.

"We're talking. Mission accomplished."

"No. About... Charles. And the money."

"I've already said way too much tonight," Wayne said. "Sorry."

Wayne turned back toward his car, but I caught his arm. He paused, looking at the spot where my hand had landed.

"You're sure everything is OK?" I asked. "Charles isn't some kind of Bernie Madoff who wants to screw us all over?"

"I'm sure," Wayne said. "Bernie Madoff was smart. Charles...not so much."

"Good," I said. "I mean, that's not good. But I'm glad. I mean, I'm not glad, but—"

"I get what you mean," Wayne said.

"OK. Thank you. Detective."

I looked up. Wayne's eyes sparkled in the moonlight,

and I wondered how my eyes looked. *Probably bloodshot and watery, if history was any indication.*

"Was there something else you wanted to ask me?" Wayne had apparently noticed me staring into his stupid twinkly eyes.

"Yes. Uh... Are you going to the Winter Festival this weekend? It's your first big festival since you moved to Pine Grove, right?"

"Festivals aren't my thing," Wayne said. "I'll probably skip it."

I tried to hide my disappointment. "Oh. Cool."

"If I do go, will you slip me a free cookie or something?"

"For a hard-working detective like yourself, I don't see why not." Again, I surprised myself with my flirty sass. *Was I getting good at this stuff? Probably not.*

Wayne smirked. "In that case, maybe I'll see you there."

With that, Wayne climbed into his car and started it up. My face flushed as he pulled away. I had tried to play it cool, but I really wanted to bump into him at the festival.

I had no idea I'd be bumping into a dead body instead.

3

DEADLY DONUTS

*J*ust two days later, the business owners and townspeople of Pine Grove had moved on from the drama with Charles, straight into the joyous spectacle that was our annual Winter Festival.

The event took place at the walking track in the center of town. Five minutes after the opening of the proverbial doors, hundreds of people milled about, red-nosed and eager to warm themselves with the festival's hot food and beverage offerings.

The bright blue sky didn't have a single cloud. A fresh layer of powder covered the field. Long, glistening icicles hung off the roof of the gazebo. A Parks and Rec employee stumbled around dressed like "Father Winter" in a big, fake beard. And dozens of vendors formed two long rows down the field, each offering a free treat for guests as well as selling local baked goods or crafts.

Mayor Delgado had put her streetlight manifesto on a brief hold and had instead dedicated almost half of the town's winter budget to the festival. She said Pine Grove needed the PR after all the negative press following the "unfortunate incident"at the orchard.

Mayor Delgado refused to refer to Vinny's death as a murder. When visitors or local bloggers asked her about that ill-fated wedding, she told them a man "slipped and fell in the creek."

I thought sugar-coating a homicide fell into a moral gray area, but Mayor Delgado seemed to think the ends justified the means when it came to protecting Pine Grove's reputation. Even if that meant lying. Or throwing a bunch of money at the problem.

Based on the size of the crowd and the smiles on people's faces at the Winter Fest, Mayor Delgado's investment had paid off. Every single attendee looked like they were smack-dab in the middle of a memory that would last a lifetime.

An old woman took a big sip of hot chocolate and came up with whipped cream on her nose. Chubby twin toddlers threw snowballs at one another. A young mother held her infant close to her chest to protect the newborn baby from the cold.

It was all so sweet, it made me want to cry. OK. It made me cry. But only one tear. Two tears, max. Fine. Maybe I cried three tears. Four at most.

It was the sight of those snowball-throwing kids that got me.

When I was a kid, I had looked forward to the Winter Festival all year. My parents would let me visit every booth, and time after time, I would get sick on samples. Then Mom, Dad, and I would help Miss May pack up her booth and we'd all head back to the orchard. May would make hot toddies and give me a 'virgin toddy' *(which I realize now was just tea).* Then we'd all sit around the fireplace while my parents and May traded family folklore.

That year was the first time I had been to the festival since my parents died. I thought about my mom and dad a lot, of course. But something about seeing those families playing in the snow at the Winter Fest brought an extra-sharp pang of nostalgia to my chest. Maybe because I wasn't just missing my parents, I was also missing my own childhood self.

How strange, I thought, *I don't remember ever feeling cold when I was a little kid.*

I smiled through my four tears and marveled that Memory Lane can be such a bittersweet place to stroll.

But then the harsh whine of an unhappy customer brought me skidding back into the present.

"Ten dollars for a dozen donuts!? I thought the crud at this 'festival' was supposed to be free."

The crowd in front of our booth parted as a woman about my age pushed her way to the front of the line. She was short, and she had thick, curly hair and cat-eye glasses. I recognized her as Jennifer Paul, one of the not-so-nice girls from my high school. Jennifer and I had always had a bit of a frenemy-ship, as in we were mostly enemies but I still felt an obligation to be nice to her.

That's why I had been avoiding Jennifer since moving back to Pine Grove a few months ago. It had been tough because Jennifer was the only hairdresser in town. But I shuddered at the mere notion of spending an hour making small talk with Jennifer while she took scissors to my head. Especially because her haircuts weren't even that hot.

It was embarrassing to admit, but I had been getting my hair cut down-county to avoid talking to Jennifer. One time I had even taken the train into Manhattan to one of those "hairdresser in training" places and gotten my cut there. My hair had come out looking like a drunk squirrel had styled it, but I still preferred that to being held hostage by Jennifer's conversational sandbagging.

I could imagine how our 'small-talk' would go. She'd say something like, "How have you been?" I'd say, "Good." And she'd retort with something like, "Really? Even after Mike ran out like that?! If I were you, I'd just crawl in a hole and die." I couldn't do it. So I hadn't.

As Jennifer approached my booth, I knew the jig was up. I had nowhere to run, and I had nowhere to hide. So I did the next best thing…I pretended not to recognize her.

"Hello miss! We're selling donuts by the dozen, but everyone at the fest can also have one free sample. How about I slip you two for free, because of the misunderstanding?"

"What do you mean, 'miss?' It's me. Jennifer Paul. From high school?" Jennifer looked at me with her face all scrunched up like I was the stupidest person on earth.

I averted my eyes, unsure how to respond. That's when I noticed a burly man off to the left of the line who seemed to be checking Jennifer out. His skulking frame looked out of place among the buoyant townspeople. He had a dark ball cap pulled down over his eyes and a cigarette dangling from between his lips. From beneath the brim of his hat, he was staring at Jennifer in a not-completely-platonic way.

Figures, I thought. Jennifer tended to attract shady guys. In the right light her short stature and bouncing curly hair gave her a cute innocence, like a 30-year-old Shirley Temple. In the wrong light she looked like a shrunken ice queen with a thirst for blood.

"Chelsea? Hello?" Jennifer waved her hand in front of my face. I snapped my focus back to her.

She had caught me in in my feeble lie, so my next move was to feign surprise. My voice shot up two registers as I squealed, "Jennifer! So good to see you."

"Really? It's good to see me? You didn't even invite me to your wedding."

I wonder why, I thought. But I kept a nice big smile plastered on my face. "Still! It's always nice to see a familiar face."

"Every face is familiar. This is friggin' Pine Grove. I thought you got out of this stinkhole, why are you even back?"

She knew why I was back. Everyone in town knew about my runaway groom situation. Half of them had heard it from Jennifer while she was cutting their hair. But then again, I had just pretended not to know who she was, so we were both guilty.

I straightened my posture and said, "I'm happy to be back in town, working with Miss May. I get to do the seasonal décor for the farm, and I'm helping to upgrade the cabins, and I'm doing all the weddings. It's a lot of fun."

"Yeah, when someone doesn't die in the middle of a rehearsal dinner."

"Right. It's fun except when someone's murdered. I figured that was implicit," I said, unable to avoid the creep of sarcasm into my voice. It was just like Jennifer to glibly reference a tragedy while arguing about free donuts. "The murder was unfortunate. So how about those samples—"

Jennifer held up a finger like "stop talking for a sec." Then she finished a text conversation on her phone, smiling to herself as she searched for just the right emoji.

I tried to stay patient, but other people in line grumbled with frustration. I cleared my throat to move things along. "So whaddaya say? Two free donuts?"

"No thanks." Jennifer looked up from her phone. "I'd like a free dozen. You know. 'Cuz this is winter fest. And everything's supposed to be free."

Jennifer's words worked like a screwdriver on my face, tightening my expression, and threatening to make the bolts pop right off.

I took a deep breath. "Actually, all the vendors have something for sale, aside from whatever they're offering free."

"That's ridiculous," Jennifer said. "How am I supposed to afford donuts at these prices, when people like you are going back to Manhattan to get their hair cut!? I'm barely making enough to live!"

I gasped. *She knew about my secret haircuts!* Still, I tried to cover. "That's crazy! I didn't go to Manhattan for a haircut."

"Yeah, you did," Jennifer said. "My dad saw you on the train. Long hair in the morning. Short on the way back home. He said it looked like a real hack job."

Shoot. I'd been caught. Still, I tried to make excuses. "Ohhh, maybe I did get a cut in the city. One time. But, you know, I was down there anyway, so I figured why not."

"Those city salons don't take walk-ins," Jennifer said. "You had an appointment." Jennifer put her hands on her hips and glared at me. She had me backed into a wintry corner. "Way to support local businesses, Chels."

I hung my head. There was no point protesting any further. "You're right," I said. "I guess I was just missing the city. I'll go to you for all my haircuts from now on." *Whyyyyy? Why would I say that?*

Jennifer shook her head with disappointment and I felt my people-pleasing genes overriding my system. Sometimes, manipulative people took advantage of that element of my personality. I was working on being more assertive, on standing my ground, on being a stronger woman. But at that moment, faced with Jennifer's judge-y gaze, my resolve crumbled like a day-old apple fritter.

"Take the dozen donuts," I said. "On me." I reached into my purse, pulled out a ten-dollar bill, and placed it in the till. "I'll come by next time I need a cut."

"Better make it soon," Jennifer said. "Those split ends are harshing my buzz."

Jennifer grabbed a bag of donuts from the table and strode away. I breathed a sigh of relief, then stapled a smile back to my face and turned to the next customer.

"Hi, how can I—" My plastic smile turned genuine when I saw who was in line. "Teeny! Hi!"

Teeny looked adorable in a bright pink sweater and Santa hat, and her light-blue eyes popped against the gray sky. Teeny didn't care if we were a solid month and a half past Christmas. To her, festival meant festive, and festive meant Santa. I loved that about her. Teeny craned her neck after Jennifer, watching as the curly-headed devil bounced away into the crowd.

"What was wrong with that girl?" Teeny said. "I would've shoved those donuts right where the sun only shines in the shower!"

I laughed. "Do you want your free donut or are you here to talk?"

"I want my donut. What am I, stupid?" Teeny grabbed a donut and took a big bite.

She groaned with enjoyment. I knew she was exaggerating her experience for the crowd, but I appreciated her enthusiasm.

"Good?" I asked with a wry smile.

"Incredible," Teeny yelled. She turned back to the

crowd. "These donuts are the best I've ever had! I'll take three dozen!"

Teeny turned back to me, still talking loud enough for everyone to hear. "And your Fruit and Fir Farm hosts events too? Holy whiskers! I plan on hosting my next wedding, rehearsal dinner, funeral, or important birthday there!"

Teeny winked at me. I laughed and said, "We don't do funerals. But thanks for the free advertising."

"Any time," Teeny said. "Only one thing I want in exchange."

Teeny smiled her sneakiest smile. Bright white teeth bared and thin blond eyebrows raised. I had seen that smile many times before, and it rarely ended with me happy.

"Please don't tell me you—"

"I signed you up for the sled-riding race!" Teeny jumped up and down and clapped her hands, like a golf-fan stuck on fast forward.

I slouched. The sled-riding race was a huge deal at the Winter Fest. Teeny had signed me up every single year when I was a kid, but I had hoped that I would get a pass that year. *You know. Because I was a grown woman.*

"Teeny! I can't," I said. "I'm too old for that race! Please don't make me."

"I'm not going to make you," Teeny said. "I'm going to beg until you give in and say yes!"

Ugh. She wasn't kidding.

Teen clasped her hands together. "Please, please, please do the race, Chelsea! It's so cute! I don't have kids. Please let me live vicariously through you!"

"I'm almost thirty," I said. "Nothing I do is cute."

Miss May approached, carrying another big box of donuts. "Just do the race, Chels! It'll be fun."

"Come on," I said. "Now you're teaming up on me?"

Miss May shrugged. "Looks like it."

"I was too old for that race when I was a teenager."

"You were not," Teeny said. I sighed. *Stand your ground, Chels!*

But Teeny pressed on. "Please, Chelsea! Winner gets free dinner-theatre tickets all year. Don't you want to take me to free dinner-theatre? Don't you want to bond!? Don't you want to hear me sing all the words to *West Side Story*!? MARRIIIIAAAAAAA..."

"Your singing is beautiful," I said. "But this race gave me a bloody nose every single year when I was a kid. I don't think you want to put me through that again."

"Just don't steer into a tree," Teeny said. "And your nose will be fine."

Teeny looked up at me with her big, blue eyes. *Remember how I said people sometimes manipulated my people-pleasing side?*

But Teeny was much sweeter than Jennifer, and I was a sucker for tradition. The sled race was important to Teeny. And I wanted to make her happy. So I cracked.

"Fine!" I said. "I'll do it."

Teeny pumped her tiny fists, grabbed my hand, and pulled me away.

"Whoa," I said. "Where are you taking me?"

"Where do you think?" Teeny asked. "Two minutes 'til race time!"

I stammered. "No! I— I can't go now! I need more time to prepare!"

"You'll be fine," Teeny said. "Just remember, if another kid gets in your lane you've got to use your elbows. Protect your space and stay low. And don't get suckered in if one of 'em starts to cry!"

I protested, but Teeny was already ten feet in front of

me, pushing her way through the crowd so we'd make it to the race on time.

I followed behind her.

I didn't know it, but that race was going to be worse than all the rest of them combined.

4

MURDER A LA MODE

The walk over to the sledding hill — through a patch of evergreens and past a small pond — would have been peaceful if not for my mounting fear and Teeny's boisterous strategizing.

Teeny was in favor of what she called the "face-first technique." As the name suggested, this technique would have had me lying down on the sled on my stomach, careening down the hill with my face first.

My argument against the face-first technique was that I liked my face and didn't want to ruin it for all time. Teeny's counter-argument was based on her desire to see "as much community theatre as humanly possible."

In the end, we settled on feet-first, but only if I let Teeny choose my sled. I agreed but regretted my decision as soon as I saw the speed-demon Teeny selected out of the lineup.

The sled was long, skinny, and pink. Teeny claimed it had "optimal aero-dynamic efficiency." And it said "speed-demon" right on its slim, pink side.

When I approached the starting line, a row of children

— eight or nine years old — were already waiting for the race to begin.

The kids looked adorable all bundled up in their winter coats and hats, and each one had a mother or father behind them, snapping photos and chatting.

I was bloated from eating pizza and French fries the night before and I had squeezed into my jacket like a sausage. *So yeah. Less adorable.*

As I dragged my sled past the parents toward a free spot at the end of the line, it occurred to me that this was the ultimate walk of shame.

But when I made it to the last person in line, I was happy to find a few teenagers joking around with a slight, balding man who looked to be about forty.

I smiled as I got closer to the man. "Boy, am I glad to see another adult in this race!"

The man gave me a sideways glance and spoke in a lilting tenor, "Don't be too glad. I'm here to win!"

The teenagers cracked up and continued joking around with the guy.

"Mr. Frank's gonna take this thing down!"

"Heck yeah I am," the man said.

The teenagers laughed again. I leaned in and got a closer look at my adult competition. He was well-dressed. Wearing tight snow-pants, and one of those super-soft puffy jackets. And he had flannel accents on all his accessories. Far more fashionable than most men in Pine Grove. *But where did I know him from?*

"I'm sorry, I feel like I've met you before. Have you lived in Pine Grove a long time?"

"Been a teacher at the high school almost twenty years."

"Of course!" I exclaimed. "Mr. Frank! Now I remember

you. I never had you, but my friends did. You were the coolest teacher in school, so I heard."

A peach-fuzzed teenage boy chimed in, "He's vice principal now! Big time baller!"

"Wow," I said. "Vice principal. Congrats, Mr. Frank."

"Thank you," Mr. Frank said. "And please. Call me Marvin. All the kids do after they graduate."

"OK," I said. "Nice to see you again, Marvin. Good luck."

I reached out for a handshake, but Marvin pulled his hand back at the last second and passed it through his hair.

The teenagers "oooooohed" like Marvin totally got me. Which was fair, 'cuz he did.

"I don't shake hands with the competition," Marvin said. "There's too much at stake."

I laughed, but Marvin looked serious. "Those tickets are everything to me."

Marvin stared me down. I felt myself shrinking under his unblinking gaze. One inch shorter. Two inches. *I needed all the height I could get.* After what felt like forever, Mr. Frank broke into a big smirk. "I'm just kidding. Have fun out there!"

I breathed a sigh of relief. "Thanks," I said. "You have fun, too."

Marvin nodded, jumped into his sled, and pulled goggles down over his eyes. He looked like an Olympic luger getting ready for the gold medal race. All focus, sinewy muscle, and determination.

If Marvin were a cheetah ready for the hunt, I was a cocker spaniel that needed a nap. I contemplated calling it quits, but then I looked back at Teeny. Her lips were spread in a nine-inch grin, and she gave me a big thumbs up.

I guess I'm doing this.

Before I had a chance to reconsider the race, Mayor

Delgado walked a few feet out in front of the starting line and addressed the racers.

"Welcome children of Pine Grove! Plus Marvin and Chelsea! Are you ready to race!?"

The kids cheered. Marvin looked concerned. He raised his hand and waited to be called on, the true sign of someone who spends too much time in school. Mayor Delgado spotted him.

"Yes? Marvin?"

"Hi. Wasn't Mrs. Fitz supposed to wave the flag to start the race? Shouldn't we wait for her?"

Mrs. Fitz was Pine Grove's high school principal, and the wife of the widely-hated local CPA, Charles. It made sense that Principal Fitz would start the race, since it was intended for children. And it made sense that Marvin had noticed her absence. He was her right hand man, after all.

"Mrs. Fitz is under the weather this morning, so I'm filling in," Mayor Delgado said.

Marvin nodded. A look of concern flashed across his face, but a broad, smarmy grin followed in its wake. "Too bad she's going to miss me teaching all these young guns a lesson!"

"OK, Marvin," Mayor Delgado said. "Save it for the racetrack."

Mayor Delgado raised the town flag above her head and prepared to start the race. "Are you ready, kids, Marvin, and Chelsea!?"

The kids cheered. I gave a weak "yay," which was all I could muster.

"On your mark, get set...go!" Mayor Delgado waved the town flag back and forth like she was at the Daytona 500. Teeny gave me a big push, and we were off...

The first ten seconds of the race, I felt free.

My sled carved through the powder like a knife. The whooshing air invigorated my senses. My eyes were laser-focused on the path ahead of me. I hadn't felt so unencumbered since the first time I had ridden a bike without training wheels. I imagined this was how flying might feel.

The cold air hit my teeth as I smiled wide. I let out a gleeful, "Woooo!"

I was winning. I never won anything, and being in the lead felt surprisingly good. *Dinner theatre, here I come.*

Then I hit a skid of ice, and my sled spun a dozen times in a matter of seconds.

There was nothing I could do, so I closed my eyes and hoped for the best.

I opened my eyes once and saw Marvin speeding past me on his death-sled. I opened my eyes again, and I was facing back toward the starting line.

The third time I opened my eyes I was careening toward a giant boulder.

That time, I grabbed ahold of the side of my sled and pulled hard to the left. I missed the boulder by about an inch, but I pulled so hard that the sled veered straight into the forest off to the side of the hill.

I tried to course-correct, but it was too late.

Whoomph! I hit a small bump and soared into the forest, screaming "No no no!" at the top of my lungs. This was not good. Then...

Wha-poof! I landed between two big evergreens and raced downhill through boulders, logs, and trees at twice the speed I had been moving on the track.

I had been scared when I was still on the designated course, but once I disappeared into the trees, I was petrified. Number one, the likelihood of a catastrophic crash had skyrocketed. Number two, within milliseconds I was so deep in the forest that no one would hear if I screamed. They'd never find me if I crashed into a rock and died.

Just steer! I thought. *Don't hit anything! Stay focused! Stop thinking about how you might die!*

For the first hundred feet, I stayed on my sled despite my self-defeating inner-monologue. Then I hit a log that was half-hidden in the snow, and everything kicked into high gear.

The bump sent my sled three feet into the air. When I landed, my speed doubled once again, and I was suddenly on what I would call the "death drop" part of the hill.

Branches and boulders whizzed by me at what felt like a thousand miles per hour. My sled skidded across black ice with violent scraping sounds. And my inner-monologue had morphed into a mono-syllabic S.o.S.

AHHHHHHHHHHHHHHH!

I contemplated rolling off the sled like James Bond from a burning car or grabbing a branch and hanging there like Tarzan in the jungle.

Then I spotted what looked like a fifty-foot drop up ahead...straight over a cliff.

I tried to stop the sled by shoving my hands into the snow at my sides, but it was no use. I was hurtling toward a literal abyss, and I would have to jump.

I took a deep breath and braced myself. Then, about fifty feet from the drop, my sled clipped a tree, and I catapulted upward like someone had shot me from a circus cannon.

As I soared through the air, my perception of time slowed, and I was frozen in a long, silent suspension, high above the earth.

I wished I could say my life flashed before my eyes, but it didn't. Instead, I thought about how mad I was at myself. I had spent too much of my time letting people talk me into things I didn't want to do. If I survived this crash, I swore I would change. I would stop giving away free donuts to mean girls. I would stop worrying about where I got my hair cut. And I would put cheese on everything. And, and, and—

Oomph!

I belly-flopped right onto a four-foot snow drift.

It wasn't a graceful landing, but I was alive. Uninjured. Perhaps enjoying the luckiest moment of my entire life.

I let out a deep exhale and the air fogged in front of me. My hands trembled. I laughed. Then I looked up at the towering evergreens above me and screamed at the top of my lungs.

"I made it!"

A flock of birds took flight from a branch, and I screamed again, overjoyed.

"I'm alive!"

I wiped my nose. Of course, it was bleeding. *Wouldn't be a sled race without a bloody nose.*

"I can't believe my almost-last-thought was that I should eat more cheese," I said to no one. Then I flopped back into the snow, took another deep breath, and puffed it out.

I listened for a few seconds. The forest was shockingly peaceful.

Just a minute earlier, all I'd heard were snapping branches, and the panicked voice in my head, and the thump-thump of the sled against the snow. But once the sled crashed and came to a halt, everything was serene. Looking around, I realized that the woods weren't scary at all. In fact, I had been the disturbance.

It struck me how quickly the world can change, and how beautiful change can be.

That thought inspired me to find a way out of my

present mess. So I stood up. Shook the snow off my jacket. And looked back up the hill in search of my runaway sled.

It didn't take much hunting. Although I felt like I had flown a hundred feet in the air, the sled was barely five feet away, wedged between a log and a sheet of ice.

My knees wobbled as I trudged uphill, but I thought of the sled like my trophy, and I didn't want to return to the festival without it.

I pulled at the sled to free it, but it wouldn't budge.

"Come on," I said. "Don't make me leave you here to die!"

I pulled again. The sled didn't move an inch.

I put my foot on the log for leverage and yanked as hard as I could.

The sled refused to move.

I grabbed onto the sled with both hands and pulled like my life depended on it. After a few seconds, my hands slipped, and I stumbled back and tripped over something.

I fell on my butt, which was luckily too cold to feel much pain. But when I twisted around to see what had tripped me, all the blood drained from my face.

There, propped up against a tree, was Charles Fitz.

Blue face. Eyes open. And a single, tiny icicle hanging from his nose.

Last time I had found a body, I had tried to strike up a conversation. This time, I was more reasonable.

I poked Fitz in the arm.

He didn't move.

I grabbed him by the shoulders and shook.

Ice and snow drifted gently off his head and shoulders, like wintry dandruff. Still no movement from Fitz.

I was at a loss. I knew it made little sense, but I reverted to my old stand-by. Chatting.

"Charles?" I said. "Uh… Are you dead?"

Charles did not answer. And that was all the answer I needed.

Charles Fitz was dead. And he owed money to everyone in town.

5

SLAY RIDING

*A*fter I made my way out of the forest, I tracked Wayne down and told him I had found Fitz's body. At first Wayne thought I was joking, like this "I found a body" thing was an extension of our parking lot flirtation. But once Wayne realized I was serious, he treated me like Suspect Number One. Led me straight to the warming tent, sat me in a crappy plastic chair, and told me not to go anywhere.

It offended me that Wayne still thought me capable of murder. My aunt and I were fresh off solving a big case, but Detective Hudson still stationed a scrawny, nervous deputy nearby to make sure I didn't "go anywhere." I was downright insulted. And disappointed. I had dreamed of running into Wayne at the festival and continuing to, uh, vibe with him. Being detained was not part of that dream.

After Wayne trekked out to the scene of the crime, my gaze drifted over to the deputy at the entrance to the tent. He looked like he was around twenty. Military buzz cut. Chest puffed out. This was probably the first murder that he had ever worked. I would say it was the second or third, but

I didn't recognize him from the previous cases. *Ugh. I'd run into too many dead people since my return to Pine Grove.*

I sighed and felt at least four new wrinkles take hold of my face. After the murder on the farm and the incident at the local theater, I had developed a theory that every dead body you find ages you at least a year. The frightful sight of the frozen Charles Fitz had aged me at least twenty. That single icicle dangling from his nose would haunt my sleep for years to come.

When I looked back at my skinny guard, he was talking to Miss May. Smiling, laughing, chatting like they were old buds. *I bet she was there when he was born*, I thought. Or she rescued him from an apple tree when he was on a school trip to the orchard. Or maybe she was simply charming him, like she charmed everyone.

Whatever it was, the guard let Miss May pass. But as she bustled over to me, the smile on her face faded into a concerned frown.

"Word on the street is that this was a murder," she said. "And guess who the prime suspect is?"

I shrugged. "The girl who keeps 'stumbling' into dead bodies?"

Miss May nodded. "Yep. But you didn't do it. Right?"

"What do you mean, 'right'?" I asked. "You think I killed Charles?"

"I had to ask." Miss May handed me a paper cup. "Here. Coffee. Drink."

Miss May handed me the coffee, and I took a grateful sip. It was from the *Brown Cow*. Steaming hot, with one pump pumpkin syrup, one pump chai, and a whole lot of milk, with a generous dollop of whipped cream.

"You got me my favorite winter drink," I said. *And it didn't taste like coffee at all. Perfect.*

Miss May nodded. "Nothing soothes the sting of a murder investigation like a hot hit of pumpkin spice."

I tried to smile but couldn't muster more than a nervous grin. Being accused of murder had a funny way of killing a good mood.

Miss May read my mind, as she often did. "Oh, calm down. No one thinks you did it."

"Are you sure?" I said. "I found the body. And you know what they say...whoever smelt it, dealt it."

"So what if you smelt him first?" Miss May said. "Half the town wanted that guy dead."

"But Wayne said Charles hadn't actually stolen from anyone. Why would anyone kill the guy before he paid them back?"

"They wouldn't. But they might kill him if they acquired new information. Maybe someone found out that Charles was planning on leaving town with the cash."

"Do you think that's what happened?"

Miss May shrugged. "I think Fitz is dead. And I don't think it was an accident. Which means something is not how it seemed."

"But Wayne said—"

"What did I say?" Wayne approached and shoved his hands into his pockets. He narrowed his eyes at Miss May. "And what are you doing in here?"

"Just talking to my niece."

"As her aunt or as her lawyer?" Wayne asked.

Miss May cocked her head at Wayne. "She doesn't need a lawyer, Detective. She hasn't committed a crime."

"Of course." Wayne pulled a pencil and pad out of his pocket. "If you'll excuse me, I need to have a few words with Chelsea. No aunts allowed."

Miss May looked from me to Wayne, then to me, then she walked away without a word.

In one deft movement, Wayne grabbed a folding chair, flung it open, and sat across from me. "Miss Thomas. Hi."

"Hi." I gulped.

"Let's start with the sled race, if that's OK."

I shrugged. Something told me I didn't have much of a say in the matter.

"Can you tell me why you were taking part in that event, Miss Thomas?"

"You mean because I'm an adult, and it's weird?"

"I didn't say that." Wayne took off his winter his hat to reveal perfectly tousled salt and pepper hair. *A touch saltier than I remembered it, but I liked salt.* "I'm curious. That's all."

I cleared my throat. Nervous habit. "OK, well...Teeny signed me up. She thought it would be funny. Plus, she wanted the theatre tickets, and she thought I would win. You know, because everyone else in the race was a kid."

"So it was a scam on the kids?"

"I don't think there was an age limit." I bristled. "So no."

Wayne scribbled in his notepad. "Sounds like a scam on kids."

Suddenly my embarrassment turned defensive. *A man was dead!* Why was Detective Hudson wasting time talking about the sled race?

"Isn't this a waste of time, Detective?" My voice came out louder than I expected.

Wayne looked up from his pad. "What do you mean?"

"Fitz is dead. And everyone hated him. Shouldn't you be searching for the killer instead of sitting in this tent with me? It's not like I had a motive to kill the guy. I'm the only one in town who didn't have money with him. Heck, I don't have any money at all!"

Wayne resumed writing in his pad. "No money at all. Interesting."

I shook my head and laughed, annoyed. "That's not interesting. It's true."

"Sure," Wayne said. "Now why don't you tell me about finding the body?"

I sighed. Thought back to the woods, and the crash, and my midair vow to eat more cheese. I told Wayne everything I could recall, even the tiniest details. *I omitted the cheese bit, though.*

"That's a lot of specifics," Wayne said once I finished talking. "Me? I'm going that fast on a little pink sled, I don't think I remember anything."

"As a designer, I've developed an eye for detail," I said. "It's in the job description. Maybe that's why I solved those other crimes, while you stood there with your fingers in your nose."

Wayne glanced at me. He seemed surprised by my tone. "Now that's not fair," he said. "I only had one finger in my nose."

Wayne's eyes crinkled as he smiled, but I was too annoyed to even notice.

I uncrossed my legs and re-crossed them. "That's not funny," I pouted.

"It's a little funny."

"No. It's not," I said. "I thought you were here to ask questions, by the way. Not tell jokes. Perhaps I should question you instead. You said the money was fine. Nothing to worry about. 'Disperse, townspeople, nothing to see here!' Then... bam! A few days later, Fitz is dead. Doesn't quite add up, does it?"

Wayne leaned forward until he was inches from my face. "What doesn't add up," he said, "is how dead bodies started stacking up right about the time you get to town."

"As far as I recall, we got to town right around the same time, Detective."

"Sure. But I'm a cop."

"And you'd be the first cop who ever went sideways?"

Wayne glared at me. "Hey. Watch it with those accusations. That's very hurtful."

I softened. "Fine. Sorry. I don't think you're corrupt."

"Thank you."

"I'm just saying, Charles Fitz was a brick of ice when I found him. The killer obviously struck at least a few hours before I got there."

"So maybe you were returning to the scene of the crime."

"And I rode a sled there?"

"I don't know your methods." Wayne looked up with a small smirk, but I wasn't in the mood.

"Can I go?"

Wayne put his notepad down. "Fine. Go."

I stood up and walked toward the exit. Although I tried to walk with confidence, I felt lightheaded. *What had gotten into me? Why had I mouthed off to a cop?*

Wayne called out to me, just when I was about to leave. "But Miss Thomas?"

I turned back.

"Don't go far."

6

MALICIOUS MESSAGES

*W*hen I got back to our booth, I packed up the leftover donuts, keeping one eye on Wayne. The detective didn't spend nearly as long with any of the other festival goers as he had with me. Then again, I was the lucky winner who had found the body, so I guess that made me a more interesting witness.

Wayne spoke with Charles' wife, Florence Fitz, first. When I saw Mrs. Fitz — tall and skinny with a prominent nose — I immediately remembered her as my high school principal. I was used to seeing her in a position of power, but she looked weak and devastated as Wayne told her about Charles' death. Wayne was gentle and charming, but he could do little to salve Principal Fitz as she cried.

Later, Wayne spent a few minutes with Liz and some of the small business owners who had gathered at the dam earlier that week. Brian looked chill. Everyone knew he would never hurt a fly, even if that fly stole his life's savings. But Gigley was red-faced and irate. Supposedly, he'd had more money with Charles than anyone. He stomped and ranted during his interview with Wayne and yelled about how he wanted his money back.

Last, Wayne spoke to Jennifer Paul, the hairdresser slash donut extortionist. Jennifer hadn't been one of the business owners at Liz's secret meeting, so I wasn't sure why Wayne wanted to talk to her. *Maybe he wanted a haircut?* I hoped not. Jennifer would ruin Wayne's effortless shag. I chided myself for wasting any time thinking about this stupid cop's hair. He could do whatever he wanted. I hoped he shaved his head, in fact. Maybe then I would find him less attractive. *Probably not, though.*

When Miss May and I drove back to the farm that night, I could barely keep my eyes open. But Miss May's mind was churning, as always.

"I don't get it," she said as we turned up Whitehill Road toward the farm. "Who would kill a man who still owed them money?"

I shrugged and slumped into my seat. But I sat up as we approached the orchard. Someone was sitting on the front steps of the farmhouse, blowing into their hands for warmth. As we got closer, I saw that it was Gigley. And it looked like he had only gotten angrier since we had seen him last.

Gigley stood as we approached. "Thank God you're finally home. I'm freezing out here!"

"We had to pack up at the festival," Miss May said. "What's going on?"

"The cops think I killed Charles, that's what!"

"Well, you didn't, did you?" Miss May walked past Gigley and approached the front door.

"Of course not, May! You've known me thirty years." Gigley looked after her.

"So you have nothing to worry about." Miss May dug for her keys in her purse.

"We both know it doesn't work that way, May."

Miss May turned back and narrowed her eyes. "So what? Why are you here?"

"I need you to find the real killer! Exonerate me."

"Tom. Chelsea and I just got lucky before. We're not private investigators."

"But I need you!" Gigley's chin trembled. His anger was morphing into desperation before our very eyes. "Please."

Miss May looked Gigley up and down like he was a bad puppy. Then, after a long silence, she held the door open and stepped aside.

"Go inside," she said. "We'll hear you out."

Three minutes later, Miss May and I sat across from Gigley at the kitchen table, waiting for him to talk. Miss May had a tray of her famous Appie Oaters in the oven, and the sweet, spicy smell filled the air. But not even that could ease the tension in the room.

"Go ahead," Miss May said. "Plead your case."

"Can't we wait until the cookies are ready?" Gigley said. "This would be much easier with fresh-baked cookies."

"That's why I'm making them," Miss May said. "But you might as well start talking now."

Gigley wriggled in his chair.

Miss May forged on. "Why don't you begin by telling us why the police are so sure you hurt Charles?"

"Hurt," Gigley said. "There's an understatement. The kid's dead as a door-knocker."

"Doorknob," I said, under my breath. I had a bad habit

of correcting people for no good reason, so I was glad that neither Miss May nor Gigley heard me.

Gigley looked over at the oven. "The cookies smell ready."

"They're not ready yet, Tom!" Miss May poured a tall glass of water and handed it to him. "Here. Drink."

Gigley took the glass of water from Miss May. He held it with both hands, like a little kid would, then he tilted the glass back and drank it all in one big gulp. The water seemed to calm him down.

"OK," he said. "It's possible that I may have, maybe, perhaps—"

"Spit it out, Tom!" Miss May scooted to the edge of her chair.

"I sent Charles threatening emails! OK!? They were bad!"

Miss May and I looked at one another. She rubbed her eyes in disbelief. "What do you mean you sent threatening emails? What did you say in them?"

Gigley picked at his cuticles. The oven dinged, and he looked up. "Cookies!"

Miss May clapped to get Gigley's attention. "No cookies until you talk!"

"But—"

"No buts, Tom. What did you say in the emails?"

"I said I was going to kill him, OK!?" Gigley buried his head in his hands. "And I said it a lot. With flair."

Miss May got up to retrieve the cookies from the oven. "Tom. Why?"

"Because, May! I had to!" Gigley stopped and looked out the farmhouse window. "I loved working with that kid's dad. You know that? Old Bill was the most trustworthy guy in town. He took care of my money. He didn't take silly risks.

None of this 'venture capital,' 'great opportunity,' 'now or never,' nonsense. 'Stocks and bonds are like rice and beans,' he used to say. 'Can't go wrong with rice and beans!' And he was right! But I was wrong to trust that kid of his. Charles Fitz. That rat."

"We all trusted him," Miss May said. She placed the warm cookies in front of Gigley.

Gigley slammed his hand on the counter. "I trusted him with everything!" He took a deep breath and continued in a more even tone.

"The first time I wanted to pull out my money, take my parents on a Viking Cruise down the river Rhine, he says now's not the time. Fine. I can wait. Next time I want to make a withdrawal to buy myself a Steinway, he says we've got to wait. OK. So I wait. Then a couple of weeks ago, I wanted to make a withdrawal for a down payment on a new car. He said no. Again. And I couldn't take it anymore."

Gigley grabbed a cookie and took a bite. "So I sent the emails. I guess death threats you could call them. Damn that cookie's still hot."

Miss May pressed on. "But you didn't kill him... right?"

"Heck no, May! I pay taxes on my yard sales, for Pete's sake. Hurting someone? Murder! That's against every one of my core values."

"Death threats are against your core values, too."

"The emails were different," Gigley said. "They were like a creative writing exercise. For fun. They weren't a plan to actually do something."

Miss May handed me a cookie and took one of her own. "Did you tell all this to the police?"

Gigley nodded. "Problem is, in one email I laid out a detailed plan in which I led him to the forest, got him drunk, and left him there to freeze."

Miss May shook her head. "Tom."

"I know, May." Gigley sighed. "That's why I need you. You know I didn't do it, right?"

"I guess," Miss May said.

"And don't you want to find that money, anyway?"

"I'm sure the government will seize it and redistribute it or something."

"Maybe," Gigley said. "If he had it in a legitimate account."

I put my cookie down. "Wayne said everything was there."

"I don't trust that cop as far as I can throw him" Gigley said. "And I have weak wrists."

Miss May peeled the remaining cookies up with a spatula and stacked them on a big white plate.

Gigley watched her every move, desperate for help. "Please, May. You solved that last case. And the one before that. I know you can solve this one too."

Miss May looked over at me. "What do you think, Chels?"

I stopped eating my cookie mid-bite. I did not expect Miss May to ask my opinion. "Uh..."

Gigley looked at me like a baseball player watches a high, fly ball that's headed toward the warning track. He was hoping for a homerun.

I put my cookie down and wiped my hands on my apron. Then I looked at Gigley. Finally, I looked over at Miss May.

"You want to know what I think?" I asked.

Miss May nodded.

"I think we can solve this murder."

7

INVESTIGATION INITIATION

*T*eeny waved us back into the kitchen as soon as we walked through the door at *Grandma's*.

"Come try this potato thingy I'm cooking up!"

"All right, calm down!" Miss May said.

We hung our coats on the hooks by the entrance. I looked around. It was early, so the place was empty. It had a homey energy that always made me feel, well, at home. After my hard weekend, I was glad to be there. The smell of Teeny's 'potato thingy' wafting from the kitchen didn't hurt either.

We walked around the counter and into the back. First thing I saw was Teeny's line cook, Petey, peeling a potato. Petey was nineteen and skinny, and he had deep acne scars on his rose red cheeks. There was a pile of potato skins beside him that was at least four feet high, and based on the sunken look in his eyes, he had peeled every single one of those tubers.

"You OK, Petey?" Miss May asked.

Petey groaned. "I should have stayed in high school."

"Never too late to go back!" Teeny said, wiping her hands

on her apron and hurrying toward us. "Otherwise, it's jobs like this, every single day for the rest of your life."

Miss May looked at the poor kid over her glasses. "Teeny's right, you know."

"I know," Petey said. "But I'm already nineteen."

"OK, old man," Teeny said. "Have it your way." She thumped a bag with fifty more potatoes onto the counter. "Let me know when you're ready for more."

Petey shook his head, put his headphones in, and got back to work, like the Sisyphus of root vegetables.

Teeny turned to us and smiled. "You have got to try what I'm making!"

Seconds later, we were over by the stove top. Each one of Teeny's twelve burners had a frying pan on it. One pan had been burned black and crusty. Several others were wet, for no discernible reason. It was not an appetizing scene.

"What the heck happened here?" Miss May took Teeny by the shoulders and looked her in the eyes. "Teeny. Have you lost your faculties?"

"Oh, shut up," Teeny said. "Most of these pans were experiments. Only one's got the good stuff."

Teeny opened the oven and pulled out what I would soon come to know as the most delicious hashbrown dish in the history of potato-kind.

"This," Teeny said. "is hashbrown lasagna!"

Teeny held up the pan with a proud smile. The "Hashbrown Lasagna" was golden and crispy and covered in magazine-perfect melted cheese. And it smelled so good it almost broke my heart. It took all my limited willpower not to grab the pan and run out the back door like a cartoon crook with a bag of money, but I resisted. I leaned in and took one more smell and I almost fell backwards into poor Petey with his peeler.

Miss May, meanwhile, just stood there smiling. She garnered immense joy from her friends' and family's new achievements, and Teeny's hashbrown lasagna seemed like a big one.

"You've done it again, Teeny! What is this? How'd you come up with it?"

"I'm single. I work in a restaurant! All I do is rearrange the plants and artwork and try different combinations of potatoes and cheese."

"Well, this is your coup-de-grace," Miss May said. "Much better than that onion dessert thing you tried last month."

"Oh, hush up. You haven't even tried it!"

"We don't need to," I said, snapping out of my hash-brown-induced hypnosis. "I can already smell it in my stomach."

"Oh-yes-you-do-need-to-try-it." Teeny grabbed a spatula and cut into the lasagna. The top layer crunched. The cheese oozed as she pulled it apart. Then she placed a slice on a small white plate, and we got a look inside.

I squinted, taking scientific interest in this magnificent creation. "What are the layers?"

"Hashbrown. Egg. Cheese. Hashbrown. Egg. Cheese. Hashbrown." Teeny held up her finger like she was forgetting something. "But it's not done!"

"What more could you need?" Miss May said.

Teeny spooned two perfect slices of avocado onto the lasagna and drizzled hot sauce in a zig-zag pattern across the top. I reached out to take the plate but Teeny smacked my hand away. "One second, little miss!" Teeny pulled a small sauce ramekin from the fridge and placed it next to the plate. "Chipotle aioli, for dipping."

Miss May and I each grabbed a fork and crunched into a bite. The lasagna was perfect. Crispy, a little creamy, a touch salty and yet somehow light. A lesser chef's take on this creation might be greasy or heavy or just... gross. But not Teeny. She had invented a new category of breakfast food and I was hooked.

"This is incredible," Miss May garbled through a mouthful of potato.

"I know, right!?" Teeny said.

Miss May continued. "It almost makes me forget that Gigley just hired us to solve the murder."

Teeny dropped the fork right out of her mouth. "What!?"

Moments later, Miss May and I sat in our usual booth with Teeny. We each devoured a fresh plate of hashbrown lasagna as we told Teeny everything Gigley had told us. It took Teeny five minutes to stop laughing about Gigley's ridiculous emails. Then she got serious.

"All right," she said. "First thing's first. You two need to design business cards for this sleuthing operation." Teeny looked into the distance. "You can be 'The Thomas Family Detective Agency,' or 'Thomas and Thomas, Tough on Crime!'"

"We are not getting business cards," Miss May lowered her voice and looked around to make sure the place was still empty. "You are the only person in town that's even privy to this information, other than Gigley. And it has to stay that way."

Teeny stuck her lower lip out. "Sleuthing is no fun if we can't talk about it."

"Well, we can't talk about it," Miss May said. "We don't have a license or authority or anything, so we have to operate under the radar. Otherwise they could arrest us."

"No. Fun." Teeny crossed her arms.

"It can be fun," I said. "Think of it like...we're secret agents. And no one can know what we're doing."

Teeny looked up with a glint in her eye. "Like secret spies?"

I nodded.

Teeny did her little golf-claps again. "I love it! Secret sleuths on a mission, flying under the radar like bats in the night!"

"We are not bats in the night," Miss May said. "Chelsea and I are helping Gigley. We're telling you because you're... you. That's all. Now stop being weird about it."

Teeny took a big bite of lasagna. "OK. So I'm the unofficial third member of the secret Thomas Family spy organization."

"There is no spy organization!" Miss May said. "And besides, you've got a restaurant to run."

"My mom's got this place covered, May. You know that."

We looked over at the register. Teeny's ancient mother, the eponymous "Grandma," was doing a crossword while listening to a Walkman. She looked content, but not like she had anything covered.

"Besides," Teeny said. "You've got the orchard, right?"

"Slow season up there," Miss May said. "Not too busy in the bake shop. And KP's got everything handled on the farm."

"But this is not fair," Teeny said. "I want to help. You two finished the whole first mystery without me. I want to be in on the sequel! Or the three-quel. Whatever this is!"

"This is not a movie trilogy, Teeny! It's real life. We need to be lean and mean."

Teeny huffed and puffed in her whiniest voice. "I just, you got Chelsea and Petey's not— It's not the same! I'm lonely, May! And I'm bored. You saw how much time I have on my hands, I spent three days coming up with a way to make hashbrowns into lasagna!"

Teeny hung her head. This was her "Lonely Divorcee" con. The same one she used to coerce me into taking part in the sled race. It always worked like a charm, and that day was no different.

Miss May let out a long breath. "Oh all right. You can come along."

Teeny did her little golf-claps, and then took a celebratory bite of lasagna. With her mouth full, she looked between me and Miss May, excited. "So, what's first?"

"Well we can't just sit around talking about business cards," Miss May said. "We need to be serious if we have any hope of solving this mystery."

"OK," Teeny said. "I agree."

Teeny craned her neck and shouted toward the kitchen. "Petey! Bring out three hot chocolates, extra whipped cream, extra chocolate. Sprinkles on mine!"

Miss May and I laughed.

"What?" Teeny said. "I can't get serious 'til I get my morning cocoa."

Once Petey brought the hot chocolate, we got down to business. We began our investigation by narrowing down the list of suspects. That was difficult, however, because we were operating under a potato-and-chocolate-induced fog.

Also, everyone in town had money with Charles Fitz, so everyone in town had a motive. Especially if Charles had nefarious plans to disappear with the money.

I suggested that we pick one attendee of Liz's secret meeting at random and start the investigation there. But Miss May insisted that our investigation be less arbitrary than that. There was damning evidence against Gigley, she reasoned. If we didn't make haste, he could end up in jail, at least for a night or two. And both Teeny and Miss May hated the thought of their old friend behind bars. I hated the idea too, but I did think it would be a little funny to see the erudite, suit-wearing Tom Gigley in the town drunk tank.

We were almost at wit's end when Teeny asked a pivotal question. "Aren't most murder victims killed by their husband or wife? Statistically, I mean?"

"I thought about that," Miss May said. "But Florence Fitz is no murderer."

"Principal Fitz <u>was</u> missing from the sled race that day," I said. "She had agreed to wave the flag to start the sled race. But remember, Mayor Delgado said that Florence called in sick? And the principal didn't show up until way later. After I had already, uh, bumped into Charles."

"Come to think of it," Teeny said. "She came in here a few days ago, and she seemed pretty upset."

"Upset how?" Miss May asked.

Teeny shrugged. "I tried to eavesdrop, but she went right into the bathroom."

"You didn't think to bring that up earlier?"

"Plenty of people come here when they're upset," Teeny said. "That's why it's called comfort food. Nobody wants a green juice when they're down in the dumps. But Florence seemed extra worked-up. Didn't even order."

Miss May shook her head, like something wasn't setting right with her. "I don't know. Florence has worked in the schools almost thirty years."

"Maybe those kids drove her off the edge," Teeny said. "And she snapped like a crazy little twig."

"She was a strict principal," I said, stirring my hot chocolate.

"Strict but a great leader. And a nice woman," Miss May

said. "And she took an interest in you after your parents' accident. You don't remember that? Helped you pick your classes. Set you up with that special guidance counselor."

"I remember," I said. "Still. She was stern."

"Stern like a killer?" Teeny asked.

I shrugged. *Maybe.* But Miss May shook her head. "I like Florence Fitz."

"No one's saying she did it," Teeny said.

"We're just saying, perhaps she's a good place to start," I said.

Miss May took a sip of her cocoa. "I guess she might have useful information. Either way."

"And that's all we need," I said. "A little more intel."

"We're not going to treat her like a suspect," Miss May insisted. "We'll ask her some questions. See if she knows something that might help."

"And if it turns out she's the killer, that's good too," Teeny said.

"How is that good, Teeny?" Miss May raised her eyebrows.

"I don't mean good, like, good-good," Teeny said. "I mean, good like, 'Yay, we solved another case.'"

"And we put the beloved high school principal behind bars for life?"

Teeny held up her hands in surrender. "OK, OK. You're right," Teeny said. "Florence is a great high school principal. Innocent 'til proven guilty."

Petey came over and cleared our dishes. "You guys talking about Principal Fitz?"

I coughed on my hot chocolate. Teeny froze like she was playing hide and seek. But Miss May kept her cool. She didn't miss a beat before answering Petey's question.

"Just saying how sad we are. About what happened with

her husband," Miss May said calmly and smiled at Petey. She could think faster on her feet than anyone I knew.

Petey nodded, stacked the dishes, and walked away.

Miss May glared at Teeny. "Could you try to keep it down, T?"

Teeny took a guilty sip of her hot cocoa and muttered an apology.

Miss May stood up and put on her coat. "Come on," she said. "Let's go to the Principal's office."

8

HIGH SCHOOL BLUES

I looked out the window as Miss May drove out of town.

Teenagers loitered outside the coffee shop, as they always had. Little old ladies hobbled into the diner, as they always had. The sun shone and the wind blew, as it always would.

The peaceful downtown scene gave me that same bitter-sweet feeling as watching the snowball fight at the winter fest. At first it made me smile, but then my smile morphed into the threat of an ugly cry. So I forced myself to stop thinking about the past or wondering about the future, and instead focused on the present.

I did a double-take as Miss May turned into the high school parking lot. I doubted Florence would have been at work the day after her husband died, so I spoke up.

"Why are we going to the high school?" I asked. "Don't you think Principal Fitz is at home, I mean, since what happened to Charles and everything?"

"I did think she might be home," Miss May said.

"...but?"

Miss May pointed out the window. "That's her car in the parking lot."

I looked. Sure enough, a burgundy sedan was in front of the school, right below a big sign that said, "Principal Parking Only." It was well after school hours, so the sedan was the only car still parked in the lot.

Weird.

As we entered the high school lobby, that same bittersweet nostalgia swept over me. I had spent so many hours in that place, with friends I hadn't seen in far too long. I'd have to reconnect with my old classmates at some point, see if any of them were still in town. But murder investigations are no time for rekindling friendships, so I logged that away for a later date.

Besides, the school was so ugly I couldn't focus on much else. Generally, high schools are an interior designer's worst nightmare. *Would it kill the district to put in a couple potted plants? Or a few nice moldings?* Plus, the fluorescent lighting was so harsh, I felt like I was in a teen horror movie.

I turned to Miss May to comment on the ugly interior design, but she was already ten steps ahead of me, charging toward the principal's office. When she got there, she knocked on the door and jiggled the doorknob, but it wouldn't open.

Miss May jiggled the knob again and called out, "Knock knock! Hello? Anybody in there?"

"Seems empty," I said.

"Yeah," Teeny agreed. "It is after-hours."

"This door only locks from the inside," Miss May said. "Someone is in there."

Miss May pounded on the door again. Knock, knock, knock!

That time, a man's voice called out from behind the locked office, "One second!"

The door unlocked with a click and opened a crack. Vice Principal Frank peered out with raised eyebrows and pursed lips.

"Can I help you people? The school is closed." Marvin had bags under his eyes, and he looked annoyed. I couldn't blame him. Miss May's knocking was loud enough to bother anyone, and his boss's husband had just died.

I stood on my tippy-toes to look past Marvin, and into the office. The place was empty, but papers and files were all over Principal Fitz's desk. A filing cabinet drawer was open. The place was a mess. Seemed like Marvin was trying to clean up. I felt bad for intruding. Miss May, however, did not share my concern.

"Sorry for bothering you," Miss May said. "But you can help us. You're Marvin Frank, isn't that right?"

Marvin opened the door a sliver wider. "That's right. Do I know you?"

"You might not," Miss May said. "But I know you."

"How is that?" Marvin said.

"I own the apple orchard up on Whitehill. You come apple-picking every year. I remember my best customers."

Marvin opened the door further and relaxed a bit. "You run that farm? That place is a treasure! I'm sorry I don't remember you!"

Miss May smiled. "Last year you bought almost ten bushels, isn't that right?"

"Probably more," Marvin said. "I make preserves and jams every fall. Give them out as gifts when I have visitors or around the holidays. And sometimes I sneak into the pantry and eat whole jars of jam with my hands."

Miss May laughed. "That is what I like to hear! Bring

your concoctions by some time. Maybe we can sell them in the bake shop!"

Marvin demurred. "My jam's not good enough for that. But I'm flattered. Thank you."

"I'm sure it's delicious," Miss May said. "Would you mind if we came in for a second?"

"Come in, come in."

Marvin opened the door and Miss May, Teeny, and I crowded into the small office. Marvin tidied the messy desk as we entered, filing a few papers, closing a clunky, home-made-looking laptop, and tucking a large pair of scissors into a drawer. "Sorry about the mess. I make a point to clean up at the end of each school day, but with Florence out, I've fallen behind."

"Oh, a little mess doesn't bother us," Miss May said. "You should see my office. Last year I filed my taxes with an applesauce stain on the front page."

Marvin laughed. "You, ma'am, are a riot."

Miss May smiled, "I try to be."

Marvin was about to sit down when he caught my eye. "Now you look familiar," he said. "Do you work at the orchard too?"

"I do work in the bake shop," I said. "But I suspect you remember me from this weekend. We uh...we were in the sled race together. I was the only other adult?"

"Oh," Marvin said. Then his face flickered with recognition. "Ohhhhhhhh." That second 'oh' was clearly code for, "*Oh, now I remember, you're the girl who rode her sled into the dead guy.*"

"Yeah," I said. "I ...crashed in the woods."

A somber silence fell over the room. I tried to break the tension, "Did you end up winning those theater tickets?"

"No." Mr. Frank shook his head. "Some little snot beat me to the finish line by the tip of his buzzcut."

Marvin let out a sad chuckle, then sat behind his desk. "How can I help you ladies?

"Right," Miss May said. "We were just headed over to Florence's to bring her a couple pies, see if she needs anything else. I noticed her car was here, so we popped in looking for her. Is she in?"

"Oh no," Marvin sad. "My junky old coupe broke down last week. I'm waiting for the dealership to finish customizations on the new one, so Mrs. Fitz let me use hers."

"That's just like Florence. So generous." Miss May shook her head. "It's so terrible. what happened."

"It sure is." Marvin looked away. "Some things don't make any sense."

Marvin tried to hide it, but I could see tears forming in the crinkles of his eyes. Miss May must have noticed the tears too, because she pulled an apple pie from her massive purse and set it beside Marvin. "You know what? Why don't I leave one of these pies for you? You're going through a lot."

Marvin wiped his eyes and looked over at Miss May. "For me?"

"Enjoy it," Miss May said.

Marvin hesitated. "You keep pies in your purse?" *I know, right?*

"I run a bake shop," Miss May said. "Why does everyone think that's so strange?"

Marvin laughed, regaining his composure. "You can leave the other pie here too. I'll make sure Florence gets it."

"Oh, phooey," Miss May said. "You relax. I'll leave this on her doorstep." Miss May took Marvin's hand and looked into his eyes. "I mean it. Take care of yourself, OK?"

Marvin nodded. "No wonder that orchard is so wonderful. You're a treasure, too."

Marvin wrapped Miss May in a big hug and rested his head on her shoulder. I marveled at how Miss May helped Marvin, just in those few moments, and tears welled in my eyes.

Solving murders was not the happiest hobby. But Charles deserved justice. And we were determined to find it.

As we exited back out to the parking lot, I noticed Florence's burgundy sedan was no longer the only car out there. While we were inside, someone had parked a beat-up SUV by the tennis courts. A big, burly guy was sitting on the hood of the car, smoking a cigarette, and he looked annoyed. He seemed familiar, but I couldn't quite place him.

"Do you know him?" I asked Teeny.

"Never seen him," Teeny said. "But he's smoking outside a high school, so he's bound to be a real winner."

Miss May started the bus and Teeny climbed into the back. But I lingered in the parking lot. I couldn't peel my eyes away from the sketchy guy. *Where had I seen him before?*

The answer was about to come to me when Miss May honked her horn.

"Chelsea! Let's go!"

I turned back. Miss May was right to hurry me. We had work to do. And we had somewhere to be.

9

CHOPPING AND CHEATING

*W*hen we rolled up to the Fitz estate, I remembered why it had always been one of my favorite houses in town.

A long, gravel driveway cut a majestic path from the road through the home's ample frontage. Weeping willows and enormous oaks dotted an expansive front yard, and a beautiful two-story colonial sat at the top of the driveway.

Ivy covered one side of the house. A stone walkway led to a sweeping front porch, with big rocking chairs looking out over the yard. And a bright-red front door with a brass-lion knocker was the cherry on top.

As Miss May parked the bus, I remembered that Principal Fitz and Charles had discovered Revolutionary War maps and documents in the walls of the kitchen back when I was in high school.

The Fitz family had been doing a massive renovation, and a construction worker had unearthed the papers and almost thrown the whole collection away. But Florence had gotten home in the nick of time, and she'd rescued the maps and letters from oblivion. Back then, I hadn't been that interested in Principal Fitz's big historical discovery. But ever since moving back home, I had developed a mild interest in Pine Grove's role in the war, so it excited me that our investigation had led us to such a historic home.

It also excited me to discover how the Fitz's had decorated the interior of the house. I had worked on some pre-war buildings in New York City, and I'd loved blending the old with the new. But those homes were pre-World War II. Designing the interior of a pre-Revolutionary War home would have been a dream come true. That afternoon was not the right time to convince Florence to give me an interior design job, but I resolved to keep the possibility on the back burner.

We approached and I noticed a pot of dead flowers hanging on the porch. The flowers looked spooky and forgotten. Teeny plucked one from the pot and it crunched in her fingers.

"Looks like Florence didn't get the memo that winter came," Teeny said.

"Don't criticize her decorating, Teeny," Miss May said. "At least not until after we leave."

Miss May grabbed the brass-lion and delivered three authoritative knocks. We waited, but there was no answer. I peeked through the windows beside the front door, but it was dark inside. Everything was quiet and still.

"I would say let's go look for her car, but we know she doesn't have it," Miss May said.

"So... are we going to just leave?" I inched toward the van, ready to move on to the next clue. Even though we didn't have a next clue yet.

"Hang on a minute!" Teeny said. She fished around in her purse, pulled out her ancient flip-phone, and made a call.

"Who are you calling?" I asked.

Teeny held up her finger like *"one second."* She had the phone speaker so loud I could hear it ringing, and I could hear when a woman picked up on the other end.

"Hello, Flo? It's Teeny. So, so sorry about Charles." Teeny listened and nodded as Florence spoke. "Listen, I'm here at your front door with May and Chels. We've got a pie for you. Are you home? I think it needs to be in the fridge." She waited another few seconds as she listened. "OK, great. See you in a sec!"

Teeny hung up and looked over at Miss May with a smile. "Follow me."

As we passed through a trestle toward the back of the house, I spotted Principal Fitz chopping wood in a flannel jacket and jeans across the yard. I was so used to seeing the principal in her signature pantsuit that I almost didn't recognize her. And it was just as foreign to see her engaged in physical labor.

Principal Fitz made quick work of the pile of wood, halving one log after the next with methodical precision. Her focus was scary intense. I remembered that look from the school hallways. Principal Fitz had always nurtured a positive and safe learning environment. But she had also given out detention like cough drops, and most students had lived in fear of her for their entire four years. *Including me.*

"Flo!" Teeny waved as we approached.

Florence cut one more hunk of wood. Splinters flew like shrapnel in every direction. Then, she wedged the ax into her chopping block and turned to face us. She looked exhausted.

"What are you doing out here? It's freezing! You should be inside." Miss May clucked her tongue, her maternal instincts always on high alert.

"Too empty in there," Mrs. Fitz said. "Besides, somebody has to chop the wood."

Florence had a quiet, determined look in her eye, like she was pushing her feelings down. From experience, I knew that was not a good idea. I did not, however, feel that it was in any way my place to give my former principal life advice.

"Chelsea," she said, "How are you?"

I tugged at the fingers of my gloves and fidgeted. The truth? I had never liked Principal Fitz. She was an inflexible rule-abider and had always rubbed me the wrong way. But at that moment, I felt bad for her and I couldn't look her in the eye. "I'm OK. Uh... I'm sorry for your loss."

"Thank you," Principal Fitz said. She put her hand on my shoulder. I could feel her shaking, despite how determined she was to show her strength. "You were always a good student. Perfect attendance. Well-mannered. Studious. I'm glad it was you who found the body."

The pit of my stomach roiled. *That's a weird compliment, lady.* "Uh, thanks," I said. "I guess...me too."

We all stood there for a second. *Awkwaarrrrddd.* I was glad when Miss May perked up and broke the silence. "I almost forgot," she said. "We brought you something!"

Florence seemed to awaken from a deep stupor. Her eyes swiveled toward Miss May. "You did?"

Miss May produced a pie from her purse and held it up. Every time my aunt did that, I felt like I was watching a magician pull a rabbit out of a hat. Usually it made me laugh. That day, standing between Miss May and my ax-wielding, high school principal, I held it in.

Miss May handed Florence the pie with a smile on her face. "Apple-cherry," she said. "Just for you."

Mrs. Fitz took the pie with a small, sad smile. "My favorite. Thank you." Her lower lip quivered. "I haven't had it in so long... Charles h-h-h-hated cherries."

Mrs. Fitz broke into a sob. Miss May hugged her, and Teeny joined in. But I hung back. I was not too keen on "group-hugging" my high school principal, although I could still appreciate the selfless support Miss May and Teeny were offering this woman in her time of need. It was a poignant moment.

This is why I moved back to Pine Grove, I thought. *To be with real people. People who care when your husband gets murdered in a forest.*

"It's OK." Teeny patted Florence on the back. "Hey, at least you got free pie out of it, right?"

Principal Fitz wiped her eyes. "I would have rather paid for the pie.

"Oh, right," Teeny said. "Of course. I didn't mean to imply you would trade your husband's life for pie."

Teeny had a serious foot-in-mouth habit, especially in dark situations. And efforts to correct course only made things worse.

"Charles was worth much more than a pie," Teeny said. "Even if he did steal from everyone in town. Allegedly."

Teeny would have kept going, but Miss May broke up the hug and interrupted Teeny's verbal diarrhea.

"Teeny's just trying to say we're sorry for your loss," Miss May said. "I can't imagine what you're going through."

"I keep kicking myself for these ridiculous tears," Principal Fitz said. "It makes me... embarrassed, you know?"

"Embarrassed how!?" Miss May said. "It's only natural for you to be sad."

Mrs. Fitz looked down. "He was cheating on me, May. And I didn't even find out until today. The day after he died! How could I have been so stupid?"

Miss May rubbed her head. "What are you talking about, Flo? I never heard anything like that."

"Yeah, well, they kept it a secret. I guess most people do when they're having an affair. Then that hussy showed up and ransacked my house while I was out. Looking for God knows what."

"Are you sure it was a woman? Lots of people wanted their money back," Teeny said matter-of-factly.

Miss May shot a look at Teeny. "Teeny!"

Florence held up her hands to excuse Teeny. "It's fine. She's right." The principal wiped her nose on her sleeve. "But yes, I'm sure. I walked in on her going through his underwear drawer."

"My God, not the undies!" Teeny was beside herself. "Who was it?"

Principal Fitz shook her head, annoyed. "That's the worst part. It was a former student of mine. Jennifer Paul."

"Shut up!" I yelled. Everyone turned to me. I covered my mouth, but I was too late. The words had already spilled out.

"Sorry," I said. "It's just... Jennifer was my year. I can't believe it was her."

"Jennifer with the hair salon?" Teeny asked.

Mrs. Fitz nodded and broke into another sob. "She cut my hair just last Tuesday. Cut and color."

Teeny balled up her little fists like an amateur boxer. "That no good, lying, cheating, husband-stealing—"

"All right, Teeny. Calm down." Miss May reached over and lowered Teeny's boxing fists. That moment was no time for hand-to-hand combat. Plus, we had just gotten a juicy new clue. *That, and the person Teeny wanted to fight was a corpse.*

"This all must be so hard for you," Miss May said to Principal Fitz. "We'll let you grieve in private now. You try to enjoy that pie. Let us know if there's anything we can do."

Principal Fitz nodded, then Miss May, Teeny and I hurried away. Once I got to the trestle, I turned back and looked at Florence Fitz. She sat on the chopping block with her head in her hands.

Her husband was a cheater. And perhaps a thief.

And maybe, I couldn't help but think...*Principal Fitz had his death on her conscience.*

10

HUNTING FOR CLUES

*A*s soon as we left Principal Fitz's place, Teeny and Miss May burst into a heated argument. Miss May wanted to take Teeny back to *Grandma's*, but Teeny wasn't having it. Miss May made the solid point that without Teeny, the restaurant would be swamped. Granny couldn't handle that kind of pressure. Teeny didn't care. She was desperate to parse out the news we'd gotten about Charles Fitz and Jennifer Paul and she would not back down. So, after a short but powerful debate, Miss May caved and agreed to let Teeny ride back up to the orchard with us.

Teeny and I both wanted to know what Miss May thought about Charles' infidelity, but Miss May said she needed to think before we talked things over. So we drove in silence back up to orchard. Teeny squirmed around like she had worms in her knickers and I wound and unwound a piece of hair around my finger a hundred times. When we got home, I started a fire in Miss May's big stone fireplace. Then Teeny and I fidgeted and hair-twisted some more until Miss May plopped down in her chair, ready to talk.

"The way I see it," Miss May said, "is that I was wrong about Florence."

"So you think she did it?" I asked.

"Let me put it this way," Miss May said. "Before we got there, she didn't have the motive. Now we know that scumbucket was cheating? Whole new pot of spaghetti."

"I still can't believe Charles was cheating on Florence," Teeny said. "Scum-bucket. Ha. I have a few more descriptive names I'd like to call that—"

"Watch your language, Teeny," Miss May cautioned. "The man could still haunt you."

I sat up and crossed my legs. "But Principal Fitz said she didn't even know about the cheating until today. If that's true, her motive came too late for her to commit the murder."

Miss May got up and poked at the fire. "But how do we know she wasn't lying?"

I shrugged. "Why would Florence tell us about Jennifer unless she were innocent?"

"I don't know, Chels," Miss May said. "All I know is she was out there chopping wood like a professional lumberjack the day after her husband died. She seemed like she was working through some heavy emotions."

Teeny perked up. "You think she was chopping wood to set something on fire? Like...she was going to burn evidence or something?" We all glanced at the fire.

"No," I said. "I think Principal Fitz was just taking out her frustration on the firewood."

Miss May raised her eyebrows. "So you think chopping firewood is her way of grieving?"

Teeny shrugged. "I've done crazier stuff for no reason at all."

"Yeah, but you're nuts," Miss May said. She and Teeny laughed.

"Maybe you're right," I said. "Maybe it was more than normal grief stuff. She was kind of like a machine."

Miss May climbed out of her chair and plodded into the kitchen with her heavy nighttime steps.

"Where are you going?" I said.

"One second!" Miss May said.

I heard a door opening. Junk rustling around. A door thudding shut. Then Miss May crossed back into the den, holding a few skewers and a bag of marshmallows.

"I think this debate calls for indoor s'mores. You two want some?"

I laughed. "Yes, please."

Teeny held out her hand, "Never say no to a marshmallow. That's a fundamental rule of my life."

Miss May threaded a marshmallow onto a skewer and handed one to me. I slid up to the edge of my chair and held the marshmallow out over the fire. I turned it a centimeter at a time, making sure each side charred to a perfect bubbling brown. Miss May just held hers in the flame 'til it caught on fire, blew it out like a candle, and took a bite.

Teeny ate hers raw.

I looked over at Miss May as I took a nibble from my marshmallow. "So what do we do now?"

"You're not going to like it," Miss May said.

"No," I said, lowering my marshmallow. "Don't tell me you want to go talk to Jennifer Paul."

Miss May shoved her second marshmallow in the flames. It caught on fire and she blew it out. "You need a haircut anyway," she said. "Those split ends are out of control."

Teeny nodded, "I wasn't going to say anything, but your hair looks horrendous."

I sighed and shoved my whole marshmallow into my mouth. Split ends or not, I'd rather light my hair on fire than let Jennifer Paul take her scissors to it.

Especially if she turned out to be a murderer.

The next morning, Miss May woke me up by throwing the car keys at me while I was still asleep. I knew what that meant. Miss May wanted me to practice driving so I could take my road test soon. Although I had taken the wheel during the climax of our first investigation, driving regularly scared me. So when the car keys thunked against my bed that morning, I pretended to keep sleeping. Even when Miss May grabbed the keys and threw them at me again. And again. And again.

After about five times, Miss May laughed. "You're faking, Chelsea! C'mon. Get up!"

Groan. "I want to stay in bed."

"Fat chance. We need to talk to the demon barber of Hastings Pond. And I'm not going alone."

Miss May pulled my feet. I glided off the bed and my butt thumped onto the floor.

"Ow!"

"Oh, come off it," Miss May said. "You've got plenty of padding down there."

"You hurt the padding," I said. But Miss May was already striding out of my room.

I called after her. "You better not think I'm driving!" But when I looked back at my bed, the keys to the bus were sitting there, staring back at me. I grabbed them and tossed them into the hall.

They skidded a few feet when they landed. I smirked. "And stay out!"

When I got out to the bus a few minutes later, Miss May had taken up camp in the passenger seat.

I stopped walking as soon as I saw her, and we glared at one another like we were in the middle of a standoff from an old Western movie.

My shoulders straightened. The wind stirred my hair. Miss May stepped out of the van and narrowed her eyes. I swear she had spurs on her boots.

"I'm not driving that vehicle," I said, doing my best Clint Eastwood impression.

"Then you're not riding in it."

Miss May and I stood there for at least thirty seconds, and neither of us budged an inch.

"Nice day," I said.

"Yep," Miss May replied, her voice sounding deeper and throatier than usual. "Looks like the snow's melting."

My eyes narrowed until they were almost closed. "I'll let it all melt, if that's what it takes."

I had the sudden urge to spit chewing tobacco or unholster my gun. But I had no tobacco or gun, so instead, I kicked the dirt like a bull about to charge. Or a dog covering up its poop.

Things were about to get good. Or bad. Or ugly.

Just then, Teeny honked her way up the driveway in her convertible and broke the spell.

She rolled the window down and called out. "What in the heck are you two doing?"

"Waiting to see who has to drive," Miss May said. "What are you doing?"

"I'm here to pick you up. Texted Chels a few minutes ago!"

I checked my phone. Yup. There was a text from Teeny. "I'm driving. See you in five!"

"Oh," I said. "Sounds good to me!"

I ran over to Teeny's car and climbed in the backseat. Miss May pocketed the keys to the bus and followed. "This isn't over, Chelsea."

"Oh, I know," I growled in my Eastwood voice. "We'll finish this later."

For the first two seconds of the ride to Jennifer's, I was glad that Miss May hadn't forced me to drive. But as soon as Teeny pulled out onto the street, I realized I'd made a huge mistake.

To say Teeny drove like a crazy, one-eyed, adrenaline junkie would be a severe understatement. She drove like a legally-blind adrenaline junkie. She screeched around every turn. She blew through three red lights. And she had a near-miss with an elderly pedestrian at a crosswalk.

I was so terrified during the drive that I didn't speak a single word. But when Teeny finally skidded to a halt in front of Jennifer's house, all my pent-up fear came spilling out.

"What the heck, Teeny!? You drive like a maniac! I felt safer on my runaway sled."

Teeny waved me off. "Oh you're fine. It's just bumpy in the back, that's all."

"Bumpy in the back!? We were up on two wheels for half that trip."

Miss May ruffled my hair. "This is why you need a license, you little backseat driver."

"More like this is why Teeny needs her license revoked."

Teeny huffed at me and crossed her arms.

"Well we're here now," Miss May said. "So let's move on."

"Works for me," Teeny looked up at Jennifer's place. "I forgot how cute this place was."

"Cute" was a massive understatement. Jennifer's house slash salon was fairy-tale perfect. It was pastel pink, with a little white fence and a tire-swing in the yard. And there was a hand-painted sign over the garage that said, "Jennifer's Hair Studio."

"It really is nice," Miss May said. "And it looks like she's getting an addition around back."

I got on my tippy-toes and peered into the side yard. Miss May was right. The small backyard looked like a half-finished construction site. Jennifer had bumped out her kitchen to make a small deck, but the work seemed to have stalled. Construction in Pine Grove halted during the colder winter months, but come next summer, her house would be bigger and better.

It was all so nice, it made me furious.

How did Jennifer Paul have her own house on Hastings Pond, but I was still sleeping in my childhood bedroom? What was wrong with me?

"That addition is hideous," I said, feeling vindictive.

Miss May looked over at me. "Whoa, Chels."

"I'm sorry," I said. "But it is. It's going to ruin the whole flow of the place."

"Looks nice to me," Teeny said. "Adds good square footage. If she puts a little fence on the other side to balance out the house, you won't even be able to tell it's not original."

Teeny was kind of right, but I was unable to hide my petty jealousy. "It's gauche. That's what it is. Plus, Jennifer didn't even have enough money for donuts! How is she affording this?"

Miss May put her finger on her nose. "And there's the question of the hour."

Teeny crunched through the snow toward the front door. "So let's ask her."

"Sounds good to me," Miss May said.

Gulp. "It does?" Showing up at Jennifer Paul's doorstep and interrogating her about the gross addition to the back of her house was the last thing I wanted to do that day. Or ever. Judgment was all fine and good in my head, but confrontation was not really my bag. *See: giving Jennifer free donuts to avoid conflict.*

I contemplated screaming, running into the half-frozen pond, and hiding under a chunk of ice, but that didn't seem like a good long-term solution. Besides, Teeny had already rung the doorbell. And Jennifer had already answered it, signature snarl on her otherwise pretty face.

"Miss May. What do you want?" She emphasized "you" like Miss May was the last person she ever wanted to see, but the smile on Miss May's face didn't so much as flicker.

"Chelsea needs a haircut." Miss May paused, waiting for a response. None came. "Can we come in to talk about it? We're freezing our behinds off out here."

Jennifer looked over at me and Teeny. "Actually, now's not really a good time."

"Why not?" Miss May poked her head inside Jennifer's house. Jennifer stepped forward to block Miss May's view.

"If you must know," Jennifer said. "I'm not open for business right now. Someone broke into my house last night. So I'm waiting for the police. They're taking forever, no shocker there."

"A break-in?! In Pine Grove?" Miss May shook her head.

"Are you really surprised?" Jennifer asked. "A murderer slaughtered someone on your farm not that long ago. Plus there was that whole local theater debacle. And I'm not just talking about how bad the play was."

"Hey now!" Teeny said. "That play was a work in progress."

"And 'slaughtered' is a strong word for what happened on the farm," I added. "It was a crime of passion."

"This break-in must have you shaken up," Miss May said, doing one of her expert pivots. "Forget Chelsea's haircut. You need comfort food. Why don't I whip something up for you?"

"Whatever," Jennifer said. "I guess you can come in, if you don't mind stepping over the debris."

Miss May entered. Jennifer watched as I edged past her, smiling with her teeth but scowling with her eyes. "Hey Chelsea. Were you even going to say hi, or just wait for me to fix that rat's nest on your head?"

I laughed in a weak attempt to break the tension. Also because I was too scared to form words. Interacting with Jennifer was even worse than riding in the back of Teeny's convertible.

11

ANTIQUE ANALYSIS

$\mathcal{O}$nce Jennifer closed the door behind us, I had a few seconds to look around her place and I felt a flush of vindication. First, I had been right about her bad taste. Her individual pieces of furniture were nice enough. They looked expensive, actually. But the styles were poorly mixed, so the whole place felt forced and cluttered. It could have been eclectic and classy, if I had a few days to turn it around. Somehow, I doubted Jennifer would hire me any time soon.

Second, and OK, fine, more important, the burglar had ransacked the place. Papers were everywhere. The glass coffee table was upside down and shattered. Cotton spilled out of sliced-open couch cushions. *Good riddance, ugly couch!*

Whoever had been there had been looking for something specific. But it was hard to tell if the burglar had found what he'd come for. Or what she'd come for. *Women can be burglars too.*

"My oh my," Miss May took off her glasses and looked around. "They destroyed this place, Jennifer!"

"Ya think?" Jennifer grabbed a handful of cotton from

one of the gutted cushions. "They ruined like half my crap. I can't pay to replace this stuff!"

Miss May walked into Jennifer's kitchen, then called back. "I see you've got one of our donuts leftover in here. Why don't I warm one up for you? Take the edge off."

Jennifer crossed into the kitchen. "I already crushed a Valium up in my coffee and that did squat," Jennifer said. "But sure, let's try a donut."

I stepped toward the kitchen, but Miss May caught my eye and shook her head, so I stopped dead in my tracks. "Do you think they got what they were looking for, Jennifer?" Miss May continued with a pointed edge to her voice, like she was talking to me instead of Jennifer. "Do you think they found what they wanted?"

Jennifer sat at the kitchen table, oblivious to Miss May's signals. But Teeny and I got the hint. Miss May wanted us to poke around the living room to see what we could find.

I turned back to the living room to look around. My plan was to be delicate and extra quiet, but Teeny was already on her hands and knees, searching under the couch.

"Nothin' under here!" she said.

"Shh!" I kicked through scattered papers on the floor. Based on how many papers had been thrown around the room, it seemed likely that the burglar was looking for some kind of document. But how would I know it if I found it?

Squatting down, I sifted through a few discarded files, looking for something that seemed suspicious. There were some birthday cards from Jennifer's mom. There was a receipt for a new laptop. *Almost three thousand dollars!* Wild overspending, to be sure. But far from the smoking hair dryer we needed.

All the while, I kept one ear on Jennifer and Miss May's conversation in the kitchen. May had once been a big-time prosecutor in New York City, and she was a pro at getting the truth. I could tell Miss May was in full lawyer mode, but her sweet old lady disguise worked like a charm on Jennifer.

"Do you think this burglary might have something to do with what happened to Charles Fitz?"

"Doubt it." Jennifer's petulance was starting to waver.

"Here, sweetie. Have a little more donut."

Sounds of chewing.

"These are good, even after a couple days."

Sounds of a begrudging compliment.

"Worked hard to make sure of that." Sounds of genuine pride.

"Mmmm." More sounds of chewing.

"Charles Fitz gets killed, then your house gets broken into the next day. Seems like there might be a connection." Sounds of a master interrogator at work.

"Yeah, well, I didn't know that accountant guy. And I never invested with him or his crazy old dad, so yeah, no connection."

Sounds of lying? Sounds of the truth?

I couldn't tell. But Jennifer's voice had regained its original edge. The donuts had placated Jennifer, but Miss May's questions were re-agitating her.

When I snuck back into the living room, I noticed Jennifer's antique roll-top oak desk in the corner. It was a beautiful piece of old furniture, out of place in the otherwise modern and tacky home. I tsked as I saw that the rolling part of the desk, the tambour, was torn loose and lopsided.

In spite of my rush, I slowed down for a moment to properly mourn the magnificent desk. Not only had this roll-top drawn the unfortunate straw of ending up at Jennifer's house, but someone had also destroyed it. Not to mention the irony that roll-top desks were invented to provide extra security for sensitive documents.

I ran my hands over the smooth oak surface, and that's when it hit me: *Extra security, right! Roll-top desks were full of secret compartments!*

I ran my hands over the desk's surfaces with more energy and intention. As my fingers reached beneath a dangling draw, I felt a slight give in the oak. I pressed harder and POP! A secret compartment slid open.

It took all my effort not to squeal with delight. A real, live secret compartment in a real, live vintage roll-top! It was all my interior-designer-meets-amateur-sleuth dreams come true. But there was no time to revel.

I felt around in the drawer and pulled out a handful of papers. They were mostly old receipts, nothing too interesting. I swallowed my disappointment and kept searching, hoping for something better. Then Teeny edged over to me, eyes wide.

"Ca-caw! Ca-caw! The eagle is returning to the nest," Teeny whispered through clenched teeth. *My goodness, she was not great at covert operations.* I wasn't the smoothest person in the world, but next to Teeny, I was Bond, James Bond.

I flipped through the remaining papers as I heard the sounds of dishes in the sink. Jennifer wondered aloud where Teeny and I had gone. The eagle was in fact about to return.

Seconds before Jennifer entered, I felt around one more time in the secret compartment. That time, I pulled out two passports. *Ah-ha!* Something more interesting than old receipts. I didn't have time to look at the passports, so I shoved them in my pocket and tried to look innocent.

The second I withdrew my hand from the secret

compartment, Jennifer and Miss May walked into the living room.

"Chelsea. What are you doing?" Jennifer's question was sharp.

"I'm admiring this antique roll-top," I said. "It's a shame what happened to it."

"Yeah," Jennifer said. "Cost me an arm and a leg."

"Well, that arm and a leg may have been a good investment," I said. "If you can get this thing restored, I think it's a David Roentgen." *It wasn't.* "Quite rare. I've only seen his work once before, and that was in a museum. When the Titanic sank the salt water destroyed most of his work." *Oh boy. Please don't Google this.*

"Is that so?" Jennifer walked over to the roll-top and ran her hand across its now-splintered oak finish. "I guess it is nice."

"Nice?" I said. "This thing could pay for your whole addition. Twice!"

Jennifer laughed. "For real? How do you know?"

I looked out the window, where I could see a police car approaching from down the road.

"Ah, well, gosh, there are lots of signs of a Roentgen. The detailing on the tambour. Drawers, handles. Special insignias, but only if you know where to look."

"That seems vague," Jennifer said. *Wow. Perceptive.*

Outside, Wayne and Detective Flanagan climbed out of the cop car and my palms got sweaty. Seeing as how I had just stolen a pair of federal documents from a former high school nemesis, I was not in the mood to talk to the cops.

But Jennifer didn't want to let it go. "Can't you tell me anything else?"

"I don't know anything else," I said. "Google it!" *Oh no, why did I say Google it?!*

I turned to Miss May and Teeny. "Ready to go?"

"Yup," Miss May put a comforting hand on Jennifer's shoulder. "So sorry about this terrible burglary. You come by the farm any time for a little pick-me-up treat, on us. OK?"

"And good luck with the Titanic furniture," Teeny said.

Jennifer smiled her tight "I'm-Too-Good-for-You" smile and opened the door to reveal Wayne and Flanagan crossing the yard toward the porch.

As usual, Flanagan looked like she was modeling a 'Sexy Cop' Halloween costume. Her legs were so long, they went to her chin.

"Finally," Jennifer said when she saw Wayne and Flanagan. "I called you guys half an hour ago."

"Had to stop for gas," Wayne said. "Sorry."

"That's ridiculous!" Jennifer had a point there. *Stopping for gas?* Pine Grove was so small, the cops could have walked to Hastings Pond in less than ten minutes without raising their heart rates.

Wayne spotted me as he reached the door. He did not seem thrilled to see me. "Chelsea. Mind telling me what you're doing here?"

"Oh, uh, yeah," I said. I was about to stammer my way into sounding stupid, but then I remembered my original excuse. "I needed a haircut."

Wayne hooked his hands on his belt, looking skeptical. "Haircut, huh?"

"Yup," I said. "Jennifer's not open now, but I'll come back soon."

"How about next Tuesday at two?" Jennifer asked. "Your split ends are puke."

I sighed. "Perfect. See you then." Then I gave Wayne and Flanagan a polite nod and followed Teeny and Miss May back over toward the van.

That was a close call. And from the look on Wayne's face... he knew something was up.

Wayne caught up to us as we were about to pull out of Jennifer's driveway. "Ladies. Hold up!

Miss May smiled. "Sure thing, Detective." There was a twinkle in Miss May's eye that made me uncomfortable. "Would you like to talk to all of us at once? Or would you rather have a private conversation with my single and beautiful niece, Chelsea?" She turned to me. "What do you think, Chelsea?"

I cringed. Miss May was such a graceful conversationalist, I wished she would have used more tact with Wayne. "I think my singleness doesn't have much to do with last night's murder, Miss May."

Wayne chuckled. I perked up. *Had I just made Wayne laugh?*

"I agree," he said. "That's not what I want to talk about."

"Let's talk about you then, Detective," Miss May said. "What's your relationship status?"

Wayne blushed. The red in his cheeks only made his eyes look bluer. I thought about how he'd probably look handsome with a sunburn. Then I kicked myself for thinking that.

"I am also single, as it happens," he said. I caught Flanagan stealing a look in Wayne's direction as he spoke. *Could she hear him?* "But that's because I'm focusing on my career right now."

"Your career, right," Miss May said. "Police stuff. That's why you wanted to talk to us. Go ahead. Talk away. You can start with Chelsea. Single. Age-appropriate. Beautiful. Getting a haircut next week."

That time, I was the one who blushed. "Miss May. Stop!"

Miss May threw up her hands. "OK, OK. So sue me for

wanting to see two attractive, eligible young people happy." She turned to Wayne, "How can we help you?"

"I was just going to say, uh—" He looked at me and blushed again. "I'm sorry, I lost my train of thought."

Miss May smiled. "Oh, come on, don't let me embarrass you. You're two grown adult people. I'm sure you recognize one another as potential mates."

Potential mates?! Gross. "I'm getting in the car," I said and opened the door to the convertible.

"Wait," Wayne said.

I turned back and held my breath. *Maybe Wayne did want to talk about our singleness...*

He continued, "I want to make sure the three of you know that it's illegal to use a police scanner to intercept crimes. Do you know that?"

Miss May, Teeny and I looked at one another and nodded.

"OK," Wayne said. "Because you seem to always end up at the scene of the crime."

"We're here by coincidence," Miss May said. "Like I said, we came here for Chelsea's haircut. Then we learned about the break-in and stuck around to give Jennifer a shoulder to complain on."

Wayne blinked, confused. Miss May's excuse was so genuine it caught him off guard. "Is that really what happened?"

Miss May smiled. "Yup."

"Oh," Wayne said. "Well...stay off the scanners."

Flanagan called over from the porch. "Detective Hudson! Let's move!"

Wayne took a deep breath to regain his composure. "Coming!" Then he hurried toward Flanagan. Miss May,

Teeny, and I watched him go. *Was it me, or did he leave a spicy, piney scent in the air as he trekked away?*

I was so distracted watching — and smelling — I almost forgot what had happened in Jennifer's house. Then I felt the passports in my pocket and I was overcome by a desire to open them up and look inside.

12

FLAMINGO FLAMINGO

I blurted out my secret as soon as we turned the corner and left Jennifer's house in the distance. "I stole two passports from Jennifer's house!"

Teeny turned to look at me, almost swerving into a ditch as she drove. "Say what now!?"

"Watch the road!" Miss May grabbed the wheel to right the car, then turned back to me. "Have you looked at the passports? Do they help?"

"I haven't looked yet."

Teeny turned back and veered once more. "Well, look now!"

I made eye contact with Miss May. "Should I?"

Miss May and Teeny replied in enthusiastic unison. "Yes!"

I pulled the passports out of my pocket and got my first good look at them. Neither passport had any creases or folds, and it didn't look like anyone had used them to go anywhere.

Miss May craned her neck back at me. "Open them up! What do they say?"

I flipped the first passport open, looking for a photo and a name. And when I got to the identification page, the photo and name shocked me.

"Holy moly," I said.

"What is it!?" Miss May craned her neck so far back she almost fell into the backseat.

"It's a photo of Charles Fitz. But the name and address aren't his."

Miss May reached out, and I gave her the passport. "Are you saying you found a fake passport in there!?"

She held the passport up to the light. "Holy moly is right!"

"What's it say?" Teeny asked. "What's the name?"

"Ernest Flamingo."

Teeny got so excited she honked the horn. "Whoops. Sorry other drivers, not about you!" She stole a glance in Miss May's direction. "A fake passport and a cheesy alter ego!? Hot dog! This murder's even better than the last one!"

"Teeny!" Miss May scolded.

"Oh, you know what I mean," Teeny said.

I swallowed hard, feeling less than thrilled. The passports had just upgraded our case into one of international intrigue. I wasn't sure the three of us small-town sleuths were qualified to solve a case involving murder and forgery. And I wasn't sure I wanted to try.

"What's the other passport say?" Teeny said.

"Yeah, come on! Open it!" Miss May said.

I opened the passport, turned to the page, and gasped.

Teeny tapped on the wheel, unable to contain her excitement. "Twenty bucks it's got a picture of the girl, and her last name is Flamingo."

"You're right." I held the passport out to Miss May. "It's Jennifer. And the name is 'Penelope Flamingo.'"

Teeny slapped her knee in celebration. "I knew it! I knew it! Lemme see!"

Miss May reached back again, and I handed her the second passport. Teeny tried to grab it but Miss May pulled it away. "You can see once we're parked," Miss May said. Then she held the photo up to the light for an inspection.

"This looks so real," Miss May said. "They both do."

"I know," I said. "It's freaking me out."

"You are such a baby, Chelsea." Teeny took a hard right. "Only you would be freaked out by two people who go by the last name 'Flamingo.'"

"I'm just saying, this goes deeper than we thought," I said. "And we still have no idea who killed Charles."

"I think it was Jennifer," Teeny said. "Maybe she got greedy. Wanted the money for herself."

"That's too easy," Miss May said.

"So then you think it was Principal Fitz?" I felt queasy asking the question. Sure, Florence Fitz had been a strict principal, but she was one of the few women in Pine Grove who'd held a position of power when I was a kid. When I was a student at PGHS, I had looked up to her. I wanted Miss May's answer to be "no."

Miss May pinched her bottom lip and tugged. "I don't know. Scorned lover. Classic motive for murder. But Florence said she didn't know about the cheating until after Charles died. And I believe her."

"Then what about this mystery burglar?" I asked. "Maybe Charles owed the guy money. Maybe the guy found out Charles and Jennifer planned on skipping town. Maybe the guy got angry. Killed Charles. Tried to find the cash at Jennifer's place."

"Guy or girl," Teeny said. "Let's not be sexist in the Teeny Mobile." *Right. Pronouns.*

"Hold on, hold on," Miss May said. "That's a pretty good theory. But how do we find the guy or girl?"

I sat up, having a light bulb moment. "Remember that sketchy guy we saw lurking at the high school the day after I found Charles? I just realized why he looked so familiar! He was at Winter Fest, staring at Jennifer. And he definitely wasn't a local."

"That guy did seem suspicious," Miss May said. "But how do we find him?"

Teeny pulled into the drive-through line at *Ewing's Eats* — an old-school burger stand in Pine Grove — and turned back to face me. "You talking about the guy wearing the hat from the *Dragonfly Inn*?"

"I didn't see his hat," I said.

"Big fella, wearing all black? The one smoking outside the school, right?"

"Yeah." I leaned forward.

"I forgot all about it, but he came into the restaurant the other day. Ordered two stacks of pancakes and a glass of warm milk. I told him that was the weirdest damn order I ever heard. He just repeated it, all monotone. Thick Brooklyn accent. I thought he seemed like a cold-blooded killer. Didn't put it together 'til now." Teeny rolled down her window as she approached the drive-through menu. "I think he's staying at the *Dragonfly Inn*. He was wearing one of those ugly hats they give away. They should stop giving away those ugly hats."

"Hold on a sec." Miss May rubbed the corners of her eyes in disbelief. "You've been sitting on info about a man who seemed like a 'cold-blooded killer' this whole time and you didn't think to say something?"

"Didn't seem relevant until now." Teeny pulled up in front of the speaker. "Can I please get a double chocolate

Ewing Shake, double whipped cream, double sprinkles, four cherries on top?" She turned back to us. "You really think he could be the burglar?"

"Yes!" Miss May and I said in unison.

Teeny took her shake from the cashier, parked the car in a nearby spot, and sipped down half the shake in a matter of seconds.

"You want me to call my sister at the inn, see if he's still there?"

Miss May looked at Teeny like, "What do you think?"

"OK, OK." Teeny handed Miss May the shake, pulled out her trusty little flip phone, and dialed. "No need to be all mean about it."

The phone rang a couple times, then I heard Teeny's sister Peach pick up on the other line. Peach had a thick, husky voice that anyone would recognize.

"Peach. It's T." Teeny grabbed her shake and took another sip. "Listen, you got a creepy guy staying there? You do? Is he in right now? No? Shucks." Teeny reached into the shake and pulled out a cherry. "Do me a favor. When he gets in, tell him he won a contest." She popped the cherry in her mouth and listened. "I don't know, Peach. Tell him he's your ten thousandth customer, and he won a boat. Uh-huh. Yeah. He's number ten thousand. Tell him the boat's gonna be there in the morning. 9 AM. Second thought, make it 9:30. I need time to get ready." Teeny stirred the shake and took another sip. "Just part of a little project I'm working on. K. Love ya."

Snap. Teeny shut the phone and popped another cherry in her mouth.

Miss May and I looked at each other, dumbfounded.

I tilted my head. "Did your sister just agree to trick a guest into thinking he had won a boat?"

Teeny smiled. "That's what family is all about!"

The bottom of the cup rattled as Teeny sipped the bottom of her shake. The sound creeped me out and sent goosebumps traveling from my toes to my nose.

I had a bad feeling. It was the same feeling I had whenever I found a dead body.

Almost like I knew that I was about to find another one.

13

PITBULLS AND BUTTERFLIES

The next morning I was still half asleep when Miss May poked her head into my room. "How do you feel about walking over to the inn?"

Walking to the inn meant I wouldn't have to argue with Miss May about driving the van. Nor would I have to ride in the back of Teeny's Death Rocket. I loved the idea, but I tried to play it cool. "I guess that could be OK."

"Good," Miss May said. "But don't you think this means I'm leaving you alone about that driver's test."

I groaned. "OK."

Miss May put a cup of coffee on the dresser across the room. "We're leaving in five minutes."

"Is there cream?"

"It's mostly cream, Chels. Come on. Did we just meet? I know how you take your joe."

I waited for Miss May to exit, then the smell of the coffee lured me out of bed like a cobra under a snake charmer's spell. Although I always masked the taste of my morning cup of coffee with ample cream and sugar, I still liked the aroma. So I stumbled over and took a sip. The drink warmed me. But when I looked outside at the frozen farm, I shivered. If Miss May, Teeny, and I walked over to the inn, I would need a heavy suit of armor. And Miss May had the best "armor" in town.

When I pulled the foyer closet open, a dozen scarves sprang out and fell to the floor. I bent to scoop them up. Each piece had been handmade by Teeny, Miss May, or another woman in town. And they formed the most beautiful collection of scarves I'd ever seen. Long, short, black, blue, pastel, even Halloween and Christmas themed. Some scarves had nice patterns, some were simple. Each scarf, however, had that inimitable handmade quality you can never quite find in a store. They were extra-thick, and just imperfect enough to make you feel all fuzzy inside.

I selected a bright red infinity scarf. The scarf complimented my black winter jacket and bright red boots, and the whole ensemble made me feel like I was wearing a "winter walking" costume, which I loved.

When I stepped onto the front porch, I took a deep breath of the crisp, quiet air. It had snowed the night before, so the orchard had a clean, white look, like laundry fresh out of the machine.

Except for one thing...Teeny was smack dab in the middle of the yard, making a snow angel. I laughed when I spotted her. "Teeny! What are you doing out here?"

"Winning a Nobel Prize, what's it look like!? Get out here!"

I tossed my bag on the porch, darted out to the yard and flopped beside Teeny. She jumped to her feet and pegged me with a snowball.

"Hey! Don't kick an angel when she's down!"

"Fine," Teeny said. "I'll wait."

I closed my eyes and flapped my "wings" back and forth,

creating my first snow angel in years. It felt good to make an impression on the earth, even if it would only last 'til the next snowfall. It occurred to me that in some ways that's all anyone really wants.

When I stood up, I was careful not to make any marks inside the snow angel. But as soon as I was on my feet again...PFF!

Teeny hit me with another snowball, then another and another. I tried to run away, but I fell back onto the snow, laughing.

When I looked up, Miss May was standing above me, shaking her head. "You two don't have any plans to grow up, do you?"

"Not if I can help it." I said.

"Me neither!" Teeny poked her head out from behind a tree and threw a snowball at Miss May. Miss May fired back with a snowball of her own.

Thwap! It got Teeny right in the face. Teeny threw up her hands in protest. "No fair! You pitched softball in high school!"

"Who said we had to play fair?" Miss May dusted the snow off her gloves and started down toward the road. "Now hurry up," she said. "We need to go see a man about a boat."

Teeny rolled up another snowball and pegged Miss May in the back, but Miss May kept right on walking like she felt nothing at all.

"You're no fun!" Teeny hurried to catch up with Miss May.

I stood, pulled on my infinity scarf and walked behind them. Sometimes I liked to let Miss May and Teeny chat, so I could get a little alone time. And there was no better alone time than a quiet walk through Pine Grove the morning after a fresh snow.

The town hadn't plowed the roads yet, so when we exited the farm onto Whitehill, there was white as far as the eye could see. As we trekked over to the inn, I spotted a fawn in the woods.

A gust of wind swirled the snow around the fawn and it stopped and looked around, its face a mixture of wonder and fear. *I feel that, little deer. I feel that exactly.*

The morning was beautiful and crisp. But there was a warm anxiety in my gut that I couldn't ignore.

"Miss May?" She didn't hear me, so I called out louder, "Miss May!"

She stopped and turned back, eyebrows raised.

"What are we going to say to this guy? When we see him? Like... what's the plan?"

Miss May shrugged. "I was just going to wing it."

"You want to 'wing it?' With a potential murderer?"

"Well, yeah." Miss May squinted and put on a pair of sunglasses. "Don't worry. I'll be gentle. He won't know what I want."

"Your aunt's great at that." Teeny scooped up a handful of snow and sniffed it. Her expression said, "yep, smells like snow."

"I know," I said. "But I'm nervous."

Miss May walked over and took my gloved hand in hers. "We're almost at the inn. Let's keep going and play it by ear. If anything seems unsafe, we'll back out."

I looked up. Miss May smiled to reassure me. "OK," I said.

"I don't want to back out!" Teeny tossed the snow she had sniffed on the ground. "Come on! You two always do the fun part without me!"

"None of it's supposed to be fun," Miss May said. "It's a murder."

Teeny hitched up her pants. "Whatever." She kept walking toward the inn, kicking snow to make a point as she went.

Miss May turned back to me. "This guy's got no reason to hurt us. We're just asking a few questions."

I looped my red infinity scarf over my head like a hood. I caught a glimpse of myself in the window of a parked car. *I look like Little Red Riding Hood.*

I just hoped I wasn't on my way to see the Big Bad Wolf.

On a normal day, the *Dragonfly Inn* was a postcard-perfect image of a small-town bed-and-breakfast. It was a three-story colonial with a small pond out front and a cobblestone drive that transported you to simpler times. The whole place made you want to go inside, have a cup of tea, and read a good book.

On that day, however, the scene was far from postcard-perfect.

Maybe that was because of all the cop cars that had been parked out front, or the police tape that cordoned off the little pond.

On that day, the *Dragonfly Inn* was a crime scene.

I figured the yellow tape and PGPD cars (with their stupid bubble letter font) meant one of two things: either something had happened to our lucky boat winner or our lucky boat winner was the killer and he had struck again.

Miss May, Teeny, and I slowed our pace as we saw the cop cars.

Teeny's eyes widened. "What the heck's going on!? Do you see Peach? Is Peach OK!?"

Miss May's eyes darted from one cop car to the next. "I'm

sure whatever this is, it's about the boat guy, not her." She turned to Teeny. "Check your phone. Did she call or text or anything?"

Teeny patted her pockets. "Shoot! I forgot it at home!" Teeny turned back to us with panic in her eyes. "I need to go find out if Peach is OK!"

Teeny hurried toward the inn. After a few steps, she broke into a run. It was the first time I had ever seen Teeny run, and it was similar to the way she drove: fast, erratic, and constantly verging on a collision.

"Something terrible happened," I said. "I can feel it."

"We don't know that," Miss May said. "Maybe it's just something...casual."

"There's six cop cars!"

"Will you keep it down? We need to keep our cool if we want to find out what's going on here." Miss May gestured toward the pond with her chin. "Great. Wayne saw us."

I looked over. Wayne approached from near the pond. He was smiling, but it didn't look like he meant it. "Ladies. I would say I'm surprised to see you here, but I'm not. At all. What took you so long? Call went out on the scanner an hour ago."

"We don't have a scanner," Miss May said. "I already told you that. Is Peach OK?"

"Lady who owns the place?"

"Yes!"

"Yeah. Uh. She's fine. This isn't about her."

"Who's it about then?"

Miss May took a step toward the scene of the crime, but Wayne blocked her path.

"Can't say." Wayne hitched his thumbs in his belt. "Official police business."

Miss May threw up her hands in exasperation. "Oh

right! You guys only show up AFTER bad things have already happened! I thought cops prevented crimes. All you do is show up and take notes."

Wayne raised his voice and puffed his chest like a tough guy. "That's enough, May."

It was my turn to puff my chest. "Hey! Don't talk to my aunt like that," I said. "She has just as much a right to be here as anyone else. And she has a point."

What was coming over me? Why did Wayne bring out my fighting side? Why did he look so good but make me so mad?

Wayne smiled. This time it was genuine. "I like your spunk, Chels."

"Spunk this!" I charged past Wayne and made a beeline for the inn.

Miss May pumped her fist in the air. "That's my girl!" She hurried to catch up with me, and we both left Wayne in our dust. It was an empowering move. Illegal as heck, but empowering.

Wayne called after us. "Where are you going?"

I turned back. "I don't know! Maybe I want to book a room!"

As I charged up the steps to the inn, I felt triumphant. It felt good to take out my frustration out on Wayne, and the butterflies in my stomach had turned into pitbulls, ready for a fight.

14

PEACHES AND TEEN

*T*he lobby of the inn was through the front door and to the right, where the dining room had been two hundred years ago. There were two comfy chairs by the fireplace for guests to sit in and read, along with a window seat that looked out over the lawn. And there was a buffet table on the far wall that someone had set with fresh double-chocolate cookies, water, tea, and sandwiches.

The place was quintessential Pine Grove. Quiet and quaint. And on that day, a solemn stillness hung in the air. That's why it shocked me when I burst inside to find Teeny and Peach bent over in uproarious laughter.

Peach saw me and wiped a laugh-tear out of the corner of her eye. She had thick gray hair and wore an oversized Las Vegas sweatshirt. Her voice sounded like a rake over loose gravel, but it was distinct, and I liked that. "Chels. How you doin'?"

I opened my mouth to answer, but before I could speak, Teeny and Peach cracked up laughing again. Like greeting me was somehow part of the joke.

Miss May entered a few seconds behind me and hung

her coat on a peg. "What are you two nuts laughing about? On second thought, forget it, I don't care. Better question, and this one's for you, Peach...What's going on outside?"

Peach cleared her throat and shook her head, trying to subdue her laughter. "Sorry, May. This kid cracks me up."

It was funny to hear anyone refer to Teeny as a kid. She had always been "Miss May's Friend," to me. But Peach was sixteen months older than Teeny, and Peach had always worn her slim margin of seniority with pride. Peach continued. "I'll tell you what's going on out there. There's a dead guy on my lawn."

Miss May wrinkled her nose. "And that's what caused all the joyous laughter?"

"Of course not," Peach said. "Dead guy at your place of business, not quite a 'tee-hee' moment. As you're well aware."

Teeny stifled a laugh. "We were laughing because there's a cop out there, kneeling by the pond with his, well, you know...his...booty crack showing."

Miss May shook her head. "Butt cracks. Really? A man is dead."

Peach giggled. "When life gets dark, it helps to find a crack of light."

Teeny guffawed. "I hope that cop can crack the case!"

"You guys!" I protested. "This really is not the time to be..." *Was I really gonna say it?* "...cracking wise." *Yep. I said it.*

Miss May couldn't help herself. She started to giggle too. The laughter was contagious. Peach and Teeny were two peas in a BnB, and it was fun to see them get going. But we had a case to solve, so I steered the conversation away from booty cracks, and back to the dead body.

"Who was the deceased?" I asked.

Peach grunted. "Let's just say you can keep the keys to that imaginary boat, if you know what I mean."

Miss May hung her head. "Ugh. It's the big guy? The one we called you about?"

Peach nodded. "Oh yeah. I came out this morning and there he was. At first, I thought he was napping. But who naps face-down in a rose bush? I mean, I've done it but only once or twice and tequila was involved." Peach reminisced for a few seconds, presumably about her tequila-drinking days, then she snapped back to attention. "Cops think it could've been murder."

Miss May, Teeny, and I all let out a simultaneous sigh. It would've been cute if it wasn't about a homicide.

Teeny crossed to the fireplace and curled up on one of the comfy chairs. Her small frame sank into the seat and she looked back at us. "This is getting to be too much."

Miss May sat in the chair opposite Teeny. "Four murders in Pine Grove? I'd say so."

I looked back to the scene outside. Police officers swarmed the pond, including one with a visible, uh, upper tush area. Sexy-haired Flanagan swarmed Wayne, sticking to him like snow on the bottom of a boot. She leaned against him as they reviewed notes on a pad. I scowled and forced myself to turn back toward Teeny and Miss May. "That's a lot of cops for one dead guy," I observed. "Are they all outside? Or are there some in here, too?"

Peach poured herself a cup of tea at the buffet table. "A few of them were up in his room, but only for a couple minutes. Then they just started loitering outside."

Miss May sat up straight. "So are you saying the dead guy's room is...empty? There are no cops in there at all?"

Peach nodded. Miss May scooted forward. "Any chance you have the key?"

Peach grinned and raised her eyebrows. Of course she had the key.

The first thing I noticed about the dead guy's room was how messy it was. Wrappers from *Ewing's Eats* covered every surface. The trash overflowed with soda bottles and beer cans. The bed was unmade, and piles of clothes dotted the floor like a disgusting, smelly mountain range.

"Whoa." I kicked a soda can aside and crossed the room. "This place is gross."

Peach huffed. "The guy refused the maids every single day. Didn't even want turndown service."

Teeny scoffed. "Who doesn't want the little chocolate mint on the pillow?"

"We've been doing a shortbread cookie for the past few weeks," Peach said. "The guests have loved it."

"Little mints are better," Teeny said.

"Shortbread."

"Mints!"

"Either way!" Miss May stepped between the arguing sisters. "The guy didn't want people in here. Which makes me think he had something to hide."

I poked a half-eaten hamburger on the window sill. "He was hiding something, all right. A serious fast food addiction."

"Other than that." Miss May got down on her hands and knees and looked under the bed. "There's a clue in here somewhere. We just need to sort through the trash and find it."

Something dinged across the room.

Miss May's eyes darted from the closet, to the TV, to the bed. "What was that?"

Ding! Ding!

Miss May stood up and spun around. "Where is that noise coming from?"

A soft glow emanated from under a pile of dirty laundry on the desk. I took a step toward it and held my nose as I nudged the clothes aside. "It's a computer. I think he's getting emails!"

I used the TV remote to push the dirty clothes away. Sure enough, there was a laptop under all the stinkage. I opened the laptop screen all the way. The desktop picture was of a big, burly guy holding a puppy. "Awww. Dead guy had a puppy."

"That's sad for the puppy," Miss May said. "But we don't have all day. Try to find the emails."

Ding! A message notification popped up. I clicked it and a message opened. I read it out loud.

"Vlad. Please don't do anything crazy. Meet me at the Tropicana poker room Tuesday. Will have money then."

I read the message to myself once more, muttering under my breath. Don't do anything crazy. Poker room. Money. Then it hit me. "This guy was a bookie!"

"Huh," Teeny said. "He didn't strike me as much of a reader."

"Not a bookworm. A bookie," I said. "Like... he loaned money to gamblers and broke their knees if he didn't get it back. And I guess his name is Vlad."

Peach parted the blinds and looked out the window. "You three need to hurry up!"

Miss May hurried to Peach's side. "Why? What's going on?"

"The cops are on their way back inside. Guess they got tired of displaying their cracks out by the pond."

Teeny stood on the bed so she could see over Peach and Miss May. "Shoot! Here they come."

Teeny jumped off the bed and landed like a cat. "Don't worry! I got this!" Teeny kicked a hunk of trash aside and darted out of the room. Her feet thump-thumped as she leapt down the steps. The door creaked open, then it slammed shut. Then we could see Teeny out the window, blocking the path between the cops and the inn.

"What is she doing?" I craned my neck to get a better view. Teeny gesticulated with big sweeping motions. It looked like she was acting out a pirate attack, and the cops were a captive audience.

"She's creating a diversion," Miss May said. "We better hurry and find something we can use."

I clicked more files on the computer, but they were all password-protected. "Everything else on here requires a password," I said. "Should I try to guess it?"

"You don't have that kind of time," Peach said. "Teeny can't hold those boys off forever!"

I closed the laptop and picked it up. "Should we take the computer?"

"Too big," Miss May said. "They'll know it's missing."

I opened the word processor. Vlad had saved the most recent file as "$$$$$$," and it opened with no password required.

"I think I found something," I said.

"What?" Miss May demanded.

"I don't know! Numbers. Names. Dollar signs."

"Hurry up," Peach said.

The lobby door creaked open and Wayne's voice called out. "Miss Peach? Hello? Anybody home?"

Peach hurried over to the door to Vlad's room. "I'm in the ladies room. I had stew for breakfast so it's gonna be a minute!"

Miss May grabbed the laptop from me and opened her phone. "This is the important document?"

I shrugged. *Maybe?*

Miss May opened the camera on her phone and snapped a few pictures of the laptop screen.

Wayne's footsteps echoed on the staircase, but Miss May stayed calm.

"Hello?" Wayne was at least halfway up the steps.

Miss May scrolled from one page to the next, taking photos. She had at least ten more pages to capture, and Wayne was getting closer.

So I took matters into my own hands. I unbuttoned my top two buttons, fluffed my hair, and darted out into the hallway.

I acted surprised when I saw Wayne at the top of the stairs. "Detective. Oh. Hi there." I was not a natural flirt, but I fluttered my eyelashes as best I could. It hurt my eyes to blink so many times.

"What are you doing up here?" Wayne's eyes wandered down, then shot back up to my face again. *It was working!*

"Miss May and I were looking for Teeny and Peach. They left us down by the fireplace and never came back."

"Teeny's outside." Wayne crossed his arms. "And Peach is right behind you."

"There you are, Chelsea," Peach said. Miss May breezed past me and headed down the stairs. "We were looking all over for you."

"I was looking all over for you," I said.

Peach stomped down the stairs behind Miss May. "Where's Teeny?"

"I'm right here!" Teeny looked up at us from the bottom of the stairs.

"Well, the gang is finally back together." I zipped my coat up. Wayne followed the zipper from my waist to my neck. I gave him my sweetest smile. "Nice seeing you, Wayne."

I breathed a sigh of relief as I walked away. *That was close.*

And I liked it.

THE $500,000 QUESTION

*O*nce we got back to the farm, I hooked up Miss
May's phone to the TV screen in the office at the
bake shop, and Teeny, Miss May, and I reviewed the photos
of Vlad's computer together.

The document contained three columns. One for
"Name," another for "Address" and the last for "Money
Owed."

It quickly became clear that we had stumbled onto
Vlad's ledger.

Someone named "Chico" owed Vlad eighty grand.

Someone named "Mr. X" owed $17,000.00.

Then there was the holy grail. The biggest fish. The
gambler who owed Vlad more money than all the other
degenerates combined...

Ernest Flamingo owed Vlad $500,000.00.

I felt like Mike Tyson had taken a bite out of my heart.
"Is that right? Could Ernest, er, Charles...have owed this guy
five hundred grand?"

Miss May pinched and zoomed until the number filled

the screen. Yup. It was a five with five zeroes. Miss May whistled through her teeth. "That's a lot of apples."

Teeny fussed with her necklace and paced. "Woo-wee! That is a ton of apples."

I felt a headache forming and pressed on my temples to fend it off. I kept my eyes closed and I spoke. "This guy... Vlad... He had to be the one who killed Charles, right?"

Miss May put her phone down. "Seems possible. But according to the ledger, Vlad never got paid."

"If that's true, that means Charles borrowed money from Vlad, but didn't pay it back. So maybe Charles planned to use his clients' money to pay the gambling debts, then kept the cash for himself and stiffed the bookie," I said. "So there's still hope that people in town will get their money back."

Teeny stopped pacing. "But why would Vlad kill Charles if Charles still owed him that kind of money?"

"That's true," I said. "The ledger could be wrong. Vlad's room was a mess. I doubt the guy kept meticulous records."

Miss May looked back at the big $500,000.00 on the screen. "Good point. But then, if Charles had paid Vlad the five hundred thousand, why would Vlad bother killing him? Better yet, why would Vlad stay in town after doing something like that?"

"And who killed Vlad?" I asked.

"There's the five hundred-thousand-dollar question," Teeny said.

Miss May bit her cuticles. "This is a step in the right direction. But this case is far from solved."

I leaned back in the desk chair. "What now?"

"Hold on a sec." Miss May zoomed out, and the photo got larger. At that point we could see 'Ernest Flamingo's' full name, the amount he owed, and his address. "Do you have those passports you stole?"

"'Stole' is a strong word."

"Do you have them or not?"

"Yeah, yeah." I dug in my purse and pulled out the passports for Mr. and Mrs. Flamingo. "Why do you want them?"

"You tell me." Miss May swiveled her chair over to look at me. She was grinning. I did not know why.

"Uh..." Then I spotted something on the ledger and it hit me. "The address! The address on the passport is the same address Vlad has on file for Ernest Flamingo in his ledger! 221 Allen Street, Apartment 5C, New York City!"

Miss May tapped her nose. "You got it, girlie!"

Teeny squealed with delight and gave me a hi-five. But I pulled my hand back, confused.

"Wait," I said. "What does this mean?"

Miss May unplugged her phone and stood up. "It means we've got a new lead."

Teeny pumped her fists. "I knew it! I knew this was good! So tomorrow we go to the city?"

Miss May nodded. "Tomorrow we go to the city."

Ugh. The city.

I hadn't been back there since stupid Mike had left me at the altar. Returning to search a dead guy's secret apartment wasn't exactly something I was in the mood for.

I wasn't keen on spending more time in the Big Apple. At least not yet.

"You wanna come with us, right, Chels?" Teeny asked, like she was talking to a little girl. My hesitation must have been written all over my face in big, fat letters.

I didn't want to go, not at all. But I wasn't about to give up on this case either, so I sucked it up and said the two little words that Mike had never managed to say to me: "I do."

16

ELEVATORS AND ASSASSINS

*T*he next morning, Teeny insisted on driving me and Miss May down to the city in her convertible. In case you were wondering, yes, I begged to take the train. I begged hard. Teeny's driving had been wild enough in Pine Grove, where there were few other cars in the mix. But Teeny was dying to drive — *poor choice of words, I'm aware* — so I didn't have much say in the matter.

When we first got on the highway, I thought maybe everything was going to be OK. Teeny used her blinkers, and she went the speed limit. She was considerate of other vehicles, and she managed to make it all the way from Pine Grove to the Bronx without any close calls.

But the closer we got to New York City, the more Teeny drove like a New York City native. She leaned forward over the steering wheel so far that her forehead was practically on the windshield. She honked an average of six times per minute. And she toggled between lanes like she was in a game of Frogger.

Teeny even suggested putting the top down so we could enjoy the wind in our hair. Miss May opposed the idea on the grounds that it was twenty-eight degrees outside. Teeny said it would be like cryotherapy. Miss May said that was "hocus-pocus."

I focused on the beautiful scenery out the window to distract myself from the bickering in the front seat.

We were on the West Side Drive headed south along the Hudson River into Manhattan. To my right, the midnight blue waters of the river ebbed and flowed around massive hunks of ice. To my left, the big brown buildings of upper Manhattan loomed like sentinels. In front of me, an enormous, tricked-out pickup with mud-covered tires merged into our lane.

"Watch out for the truck!" I yelped.

"I see it." Teeny laid on the horn, sped up, and cut the pickup off. "Take that, Truckboy."

Miss May laughed. "Truckboy?"

I tightened my seatbelt as Teeny turned off the highway and into the city. That's when the true mayhem began.

Seconds later, we were in the heart of midtown Manhattan...the part near Times Square. With the giant buildings. And the cabbies. And the people scurrying like ants. And the worst traffic you've ever seen.

Miss May let out a satisfied sigh. "Ah, the city! Doesn't it just make you glad to be alive?"

"It makes me scared for my life," I said. *Especially with Teeny's driving.* "Watch out! Person!"

"I see her." Teeny slammed on her brakes. A delivery guy darted across the road, not even bothering to wave thanks. "Stupid jaybirds!"

"Jaywalkers," I muttered under my breath. The correction slipped out, but I did not want Teeny to hear me sass her while she was driving. "And why are we in midtown, anyway? Flamingo's address is all the way down in the village."

"I'm jumping out for a slice of white!" Teeny pulled over right beneath a giant "No Parking" sign, put on her hazards, and jumped out of the convertible. "See you in five!"

Teeny darted toward a spot called *John's Pizza* about a block down the road. I knew the place. I had gone there with Mike on one of our first dates. Long before he became the runaway-fiancé.

As I watched Teeny hustle inside *John's*, my stomach contracted like over-kneaded dough. "Mike loved the meatball calzone at that place," I whined. "And the sauce. He used to ask for a gallon of sauce to take home, but they would only bring him a little container. They thought he was exaggerating but he wasn't."

"It's a good spot." Miss May said. She didn't like to engage on the topic of Mike or the shipwreck of my relationship. "But that guy was a rotten apple."

"Orchard humor. Nice."

"I do what I can."

I gnawed at the jagged cuticle by my thumbnail. "What if I see him in the city?" *That thought hadn't occurred to me!* "Oh no, what if I run into Mike?!"

"Ten million people. Not likely. Besides, you look nice today. He'd be kicking himself if he saw you walk by. "

I scoffed, "Yeah, right."

"Give yourself some credit, Chels."

A young couple strolled by my window, holding hands and laughing so hard they were almost crying. They stopped walking and hugged, still shaking with laughter.

"Look at those two," I said, pointing to the couple. "Mike and I never laughed like that." My words hung in the air. *Huh. Mike and I never laughed like that.* Who cared whether or not he liked the meatballs? Mike didn't deserve a gallon of sauce! He didn't deserve any sauce. Not even a spoonful.

Miss May was right. I should give myself some credit. I wasn't the same girl Mike had abandoned at the altar. I was growing. Slow-growing, but it still counted.

Teeny shuffled back to the car, empty-handed.

"Where's your slice of white?" I asked.

"Already ate it!" Teeny boasted.

"What about our slices?" Miss May said.

Teeny slumped over. "I forgot to get you anything! I guess I'll go back, if I absolutely, positively have to."

Miss May grinned, enjoying Teeny's act. "I'll take a slice of Sicilian, please."

Teeny huffed and hurried back toward the restaurant.

"I'll take plain cheese!" I yelled after her.

Half an hour later, Teeny parallel parked right in front of Ernest Flamingo's secret apartment, and scoped it out from the street.

The building was six stories tall and brick. Bright graffiti decorated the top level. And a Chinese barbershop occupied the first floor, signage written in Cantonese. An elderly Asian man sat on a stool out front, sleeping.

Miss May tried the door to the apartment building, but it didn't budge. "It's locked," she said.

Teeny craned her neck up at the building. "Then how are we going to get up there?"

The sleeping man stirred and grumbled, "Just buzz numbers! Someone let you in." Then he went right back to sleep.

"Buzz numbers," Miss May said. "Not sure what that means."

"I think I know," I said. "Can I try something? My friends used to do this when they got locked out of a party."

Miss May stepped aside. "Have at it."

There was an intercom system mounted on the wall beside the entrance. I opened the metal flap and pressed the buzzer for every apartment in the building at the same time. *Just buzz numbers.*

"Ohhhhh," Teeny said. "Smart. But no one will let you in just because you—"

BZZZ. The door unlocked. I held it open, and Miss May and Teeny walked through, smiling. For once, I was the one who knew how to do something, and I beamed with pride.

I looked around as we entered the building. A bearded hipster wrestled with his overflowing mailbox. An old lady in pajamas shuffled out to the dumpsters with a bag of trash. The building and its occupants felt exceptionally normal.

I glanced at Miss May. "This building seems...standard. Is it possible Charles just had an apartment in the city, and there's nothing more to it than that?"

Miss May crossed to the rickety elevator bank and pressed the call button. "You mean Ernest Flamingo? Doubt it."

"I bet this is where he hid the bodies," Teeny said.

Ding. The elevator arrived. I stepped on and held the door open for Teeny and Miss May. "I doubt Charles had any bodies."

"But if he did, I bet he kept them here!" Teeny's eyes widened.

"Why would he rent out an apartment to stash bodies?" I

asked. "These apartments are tiny. The whole place would reek in a matter of days."

"Oh," Teeny hung her head. "I hadn't considered that."

Miss May hit the number five on the elevator and it creaked to life. As it rattled upwards, we all tensed and held onto the small side railing. The elevator was terrifying. Someone had scratched their graffiti tags into the walls and onto the ceiling. Bars protected a little window in the door. And the light flickered every time we passed a new floor. It was like a bad amusement park ride.

Miss May, Teeny and I exchanged creeped-out looks as we rode up to the fifth floor. Then, when the elevator dinged again, we tripped over one another in a race to make it out into the hall. Teeny opened her mouth to complain about the elevator, but Miss May held up a finger.

"Shh." Miss May pointed toward the end of the hall. "There's the apartment. End of the hall."

Teeny and I swiveled our heads toward Miss May. She was right. There was apartment 5C. And the door was already open a crack. "Is it me, or is that door open a—"

Miss May pressed her finger to her lips to make sure Teeny and I stayed quiet. Then she moved toward the apartment, like she was tip-toeing past a sleeping guard. Each careful footstep echoed in the empty hall, and the street sounds outside faded to a muted din.

I wanted to follow Miss May. To be her backup. But my nerves had seized control of my body. *What if someone was hiding in that apartment? What if there really were dead bodies in there? What if the place was haunted?*

Miss May arrived at the door. Reached out. Nudged it open with her pointer finger. She turned back to us and whispered, "I hear something. Inside."

Teeny and I took a step forward and listened. Miss May

was right. A faint scratching noise rose from inside the apartment.

Almost like someone was clawing at the wood floors.

Scritch-scritch-scritch. Scritch-scritch-scritch.

I tapped Miss May on the shoulder. "We should turn back."

Miss May shook her head and smoothed her shirt. "We can't do that. Not now."

"Then let's call the cops."

Miss May stared at me. "How would you explain our presence here to an officer of the law?"

She had me there. Miss May nudged the door open further and stepped toward the door.

We stepped into the foyer and whoosh!

Something darted out of the apartment and into the hall.

I shrieked. Teeny grabbed her chest. Miss May thudded back against the wall.

"What was that!?" I peered out into the hall and what I saw made me laugh so hard I almost cried. Teeny and Miss May poked their heads out beside mine.

"What was it!?" Miss May asked. "Why are you laughing?"

"Look!" I pointed at the stairwell. A squirrel perched on the railing, big round eyes trained on us. He squeaked in his chirpy squirrel voice and flicked his bushy tail.

"A squirrel in an apartment!" Miss May chuckled. "I thought we were in the city, not the country!"

Teeny approached the squirrel with an outstretched hand. "Awww, he's so cute! Look at him!"

Teeny took one more step, and the squirrel leapt off the banister, right at her face. Teeny stumbled back, swatting at the squirrel. "May! Get it off me! Help!"

The squirrel scampered over Teeny's shoulder, tail wiggling, then it paused on her shoulder before diving off her back and disappearing down the stairs. Teeny yelled after the squirrel, "And don't come back!"

The three of us stood in the hallway, hunched over and holding our stomachs as we tried to recover from our laughter. It took over a minute, but once we calmed down, we remembered the scary apartment and the fact that we were there to investigate a murder.

Miss May nudged the door open again.

Teeny hesitated. "Hold on now. There could be a whole family of bushy-tailed assassins in there."

Miss May stepped into the apartment. "I think we'll survive."

Miss May flicked the light on. Teeny and I entered behind Miss May, and we all inspected our surroundings.

The place was like the apartment version of the elevator we had enjoyed on the way up.

A fluorescent light buzzed overhead. Electrician's tape held together a ratty couch. An inflatable bed oozed air when I stepped on it. And papers littered the floor.

Teeny took another step inside. "Looks like he could have used your interior decorating services, Chels."

"This place needs a demolition man, not a decorator," I said.

Miss May nodded. "Someone ransacked this apartment. Just like Jennifer's house." She moved some papers aside with her foot. "Must have been our good friend Vlad. He did have the address in his file."

I walked into the kitchen. A half-eaten can of mushy spaghetti was open on the counter. "But this whole apartment just makes me more confused," I said as I strolled back out to the living room. "Why would Charles live like this, if he had stolen money from everyone in town?"

Miss May turned up her palms. "Maybe he crashed here when he came to the city to gamble."

Teeny picked up a piece of paper off the floor. "Do you think perhaps these bank records will help us figure it out?" Teeny squatted and sorted through more papers. "Or these records? Or these!?"

Teeny handed me the papers, and I checked them out. *Sure enough, these were bank records.* I shook my head. "Who gets printed bank records anymore?"

"That's a good point." Teeny stepped closer to get a look at the document. "Even I do my banking online, and I'm older than sand." She waited a few seconds, then threw up her arms. "Really? No objections to me being older than sand?"

Miss May and I talked over each other, scrambling to soothe Teeny's ego. "You look very young!" "Sand is way older than you." "How old are you again? In your thirties right?" "You could play a twenty-something on TV."

"Oh, stop," Teeny said. But she clearly liked it.

Miss May picked up a bank record and took a close look. "Hmmm. I have an idea why someone might have printed records. If you print them out, they're easier to fake."

I scanned the page I was holding. It looked like an official document from the Bank of Pine Grove. The account belonged to Fitz & Son Wealth Management, and the balance was big. $1,345,534.00 big. "This looks real," I said. "Man, Charles was looking after a lot of money."

"Look closer," Miss May stepped toward me. "There's a mistake on the balance report."

I held the statement up by the window, so I could get a better look. "I don't see it."

"Yes, you do. Look on top. See the address of the bank?"

I scanned for the address and found it. "Yeah. What's wrong with it?"

Miss May pointed at the paper I held. "ZIP code says 10596."

I shrugged. "So what? That's the ZIP code in Pine Grove."

Miss May shook her head. "You would think so, wouldn't you? And ninety-nine percent of town is in that ZIP. But the bank? The bank is in 10958."

"But—"

"Small town. I know. That's why most people assume we've only got one ZIP," Miss May seemed pleased with her intimate knowledge of the mail. "But when they rezoned us in the eighties... It doesn't matter. Point is: wrong ZIP."

Teeny came over and peered over my shoulder. "She's right. He slipped on the ZIP. That little sneak was a forger, too!"

I still didn't understand. "But why would Fitz fake bank records that show he has all that money?"

"Why do you think?" Miss May said. "What did Charles have to gain by pretending he still had the money?"

I gasped. "Everyone would leave him alone. And leave their money alone too!" My mouth hung open. "Do you think these records are what Charles showed to the cops when he wanted to prove he still had everyone's money?"

Miss May stood. "That's exactly what I think. Which would also explain this..."

Miss May handed me a post-it note. A few dozen random characters were scrawled on top. Some capital letters. Some lower case. Plus numbers and symbols and punctuation. It looked like the most complicated password ever created. Below that was a dollar amount.

$1,345,534.00. The same amount listed on the falsified bank statement.

I dropped the post-it, and it fluttered to the floor. "He moved the money."

Miss May tapped her nose three times. "And where'd he move it?"

I scratched my ear. "I have no idea. I don't know how to move money! I only know how to accidentally lose it."

Teeny peeled the post-it up off the floor. "This could be the combination to a hi-tech safe."

"Ooooh, a safe," I said. "That's smart."

Miss May shook her head. I could tell she was having fun teasing out this mystery even though it involved her missing money.

"Then just tell us," I said. "What's with the note!"

"No, no! We can figure it out." Teeny paced back and forth and muttered to herself. I picked up a few more pieces of paper to hunt for a new clue, but there was nothing left except junk mail and coupons.

There was a twenty-percent-off coupon for a bed and bath store. There was a ten-percent-off coupon for a three topping pizza if you bought a drink. There was a big, full-page ad for a sale on Swiss cheese at the local grocery story.

I threw the papers down in frustration. I wasn't in the mood to play games, and I didn't know why Miss May was toying with us. I looked down at the coupons and stuck out my lower lip.

"Will you just tell us?! There's nothing here but expired discounts for Swiss cheese!" *Stupid Switzerland, with their cheese and their neutrality, and their fancy secret banks.* Fancy banks, that was it! I jumped up and down in excitement. "I got it! The money's in a Swiss bank! It's the number to a secret account!"

Miss May smiled. "Ding ding ding! The account may not be Swiss, but it's definitely overseas."

Teeny smacked my arm. "I was about to say that!"

Miss May scooped up every piece of paper on the floor and folded the whole pile up.

"Most of that is junk." I handed Miss may the ad for Swiss cheese. "See?"

"Still." Miss May shoved the papers in her pocket and zipped up her coat. "You never know what might be a clue."

Miss May zipped her coat and pulled on her hat.

I looked around the seedy studio and contemplated what our next move might be. "All right. So now we know Charles had the money, right?"

"Heck yeah, we do!" Teeny gave me a fist-bump and I giggled. "And it's out there, in a secret account!"

"That's what we think," Miss May said. "And this is good. It's a good step." Miss May exhaled. "But we still have to figure out who killed Charles, who killed the bookie, and how we're going to find that money and get it back."

Miss May strode out of the apartment, and I felt like her exit was the punctuation mark of her previous sentence. But I wasn't sure if her departure was an exclamation point, or a comma, or a period, or what. Maybe it was an ellipsis...

Miss May turned back and called out, "I'm taking the stairs back down!"

Teeny hurried toward the door. "Me too! Come on, Chels."

"Coming. Just give me a second." Teeny was already out in the hall. I was left alone in the apartment.

Looking around at the junk mail and the crappy couch, it reminded me of my old place in Jersey City. I had hated that apartment, and I had felt like a prisoner between those four dingy walls. *Sometimes*, I thought, *we trap ourselves in lives we don't want.* I felt lucky. I wasn't trapped anymore. Then my heart swelled with surprising sympathy for the late Charles Fitz, CPA. He might have been a thief and a cheat, but he must have been trapped too. And he'd taken the hard way out.

I turned out the lights and exited. Whatever was coming next, I felt ready. But I had no idea how ready I would need to be.

17

POT ROAST AND PLANNING

*T*he next night, Miss May made a big dinner and invited Gigley over to give him an update on the case. Miss May told Gigley every detail as we ate a nice pot roast with potatoes and gravy. And although Miss May tried to be succinct, Gigley interrupted every thirty seconds with a clarifying question.

"What kind of computer did this Vlad use?"

"Where was this secret apartment?"

"Are you sure you saw a squirrel, or could it have been a chipmunk?"

Over an hour later, Miss May got to the part about the post-it note with the number for the overseas bank account. She pulled the note out of the stack of papers she'd taken from Charles' apartment and handed it to Gigley.

"Can you make anything of this?" she asked. "I never had to deal with any anonymous banks in my practice, but I figured you may have."

"I have." Gigley took a sip of wine. "Once. With a client."

"Who was it?" I scooted to the edge of my seat.

"They prefer anonymity." Gigley put on his reading glasses and held the post-it up to his face. "Hence the secret account."

"That makes sense. Dumb question." *Didn't have to make me feel even dumber though.*

Gigley looked over the note for a few seconds. "Yep. This is an overseas bank account number. At least I think it is." He lowered the note and took off his glasses. "Problem is, that's all I know."

Miss May cracked a knuckle. "That's what I feared."

Gigley ran his thumb over the note on the table. "Did you bring any of this to the cops? Or that new detective? What's his name?"

"Wayne," I said, a little too much enthusiasm. "Er, Detective Wayne Hudson."

Miss May side-eyed me, then turned back to Gigley. "I haven't looped in the police. No."

"Good. Don't."

I looked at Gigley in surprise. He was by far the most law-abiding citizen of Pine Grove, so his desire to keep something from the police was way out of character. "Why not?"

"This kind of money, you never know who you can trust." Gigley ripped into a piece of roast and swallowed it in one bite. "Especially when it comes to the authorities."

"You're right about that." Miss May buttered a small hunk of bread.

"Besides, you two are better cops than those cops will ever be," Gigley said, gesturing at me and Miss May.

Miss May waved Gigley away with a dismissive flick of the wrist. "That's not saying much around here."

"Wayne seems like a decent cop to me," I said.

"Decent being the operative word." Gigley took another big bite of roast. "When it comes to my money and my town? I want way better than decent."

"Amen to that." Miss May put her fork down. "How did I ever trust Charles Fitz? Remember what a terror he was as a teenager?"

Gigley nodded. "Egged my house every year at Halloween. Ten years straight. With hundreds of eggs!"

Miss May pushed her plate away, annoyed. She looked down. I could sense her energy shifting, and my energy was a notorious copycat.

"Miss May, are you OK?" I prodded.

"I'm fine." She angled herself away from me and Gigley. "I'm embarrassed, that's all." Miss May dabbed the corners of her eyes with a napkin. I sat forward to get a closer look. Is that... Could Miss May... Was she crying?

I wanted to help, but I didn't know what to do. Miss May was rarely vulnerable, even around me. But here she was, busting a leak in front of Gigley? How much money did she stand to lose?

I looked over at Gigley for help. He shrugged. Gigley was a very smart man, but his emotional IQ rested somewhere in the low teens.

Miss May sniffled. "That money was everything I had for retirement. Every penny."

Gigley lowered his fork. "It's not your fault, May. He got me too."

"He got me worse!" Miss May raised her voice. "I'm sorry. I didn't... I didn't mean to snap."

"I get it." Gigley said. "You know I do."

Miss May nodded. Dabbed her eyes again. "I wanted to leave that money to Chelsea one day. You know?"

I swiveled to my aunt, touched and upset at the idea that Miss May would ever leave me anything. "Miss May. I don't need your money."

"Well, I wanted you to have it!" Miss May banged her glass down on the table.

"May. Calm down." Gigley reached across the table and rested his hand on her arm. "We're going to get that money back. No doubt about it. I've got the best investigators in all of Pine Grove on the case."

Miss May picked at the tablecloth. "Best investigators, my left boot. I thought we were on the cusp of a break-through. But what do we have? An anonymous bank account. A coupon for Swiss cheese. And an extra dead guy we've never even met."

"It sounds to me like you've got a whole big pile of clues, May. And all you have to do is follow them." Gigley voice was soft and calm. "If I could, I'd join you."

"Why can't you?" I asked. "Because you sent all those threatening emails?"

"Thank you for reminding me, Chelsea. That's partially it. I also have a law firm to run." Gigley patted Miss May's shoulder. "You just need to do what you always do. Assess the situation, pick a course of action, and pursue it."

Miss May sniffled one last time. "Thank you, Tom." She turned to Gigley with a small smile. "You're right. And I think I know exactly what we need to do next."

"You do?" I didn't mean to sound incredulous, but I had no idea what we needed to do next.

Miss May nodded, then looked up. "And I'll tell you. Just as soon as soon as you clear the table and help me serve dessert."

"Oh come on!" I pushed my chair back. No point arguing with Miss May.

Gigley laughed and rested his hands on his stomach. "Good to have you back, May." I started to clear the table, and Gigley chuckled again. "Good to have you back."

18

TINY HORSE THERAPY

I was still full from pot roast when Miss May and I arrived at *Grandma's* the next morning. But when we entered the restaurant, and I caught a whiff of Teeny's fresh-baked hashbrown lasagna (#HBL on social media), my hunger awoke like a dragon from a long slumber.

From the looks of it, I wasn't the only one with a hunger dragon.

Out-of-towners packed the restaurant, lining the vestibule as they waited for tables. The patrons buzzed in happy conversation and snapped photos of their #HBL. Granny perched on her usual stool, oblivious to the increase in business. The place felt so warm and cozy, I felt guilty for showing up with news about a murder investigation.

Miss May flagged Teeny down as Teeny bustled toward the kitchen with a stack of dishes.

"What happened here!?" Miss May gestured to the crowd. "You get a write up in the New York Times?"

"Better." Teeny pointed at something under a table. A kid was on his back, pulling gum off the back of an out-of-commission table. "Petey put some type of video on his Internet, and it turned into a virus."

"It went 'viral.'" Petey pulled a long strand of blue gum off the table and flicked it into a bucket.

"Viral. That's right. You are so smart, Petey. Might be good to finish high school and get a real job that will make your parents proud."

Petey grimaced and scraped at a new piece of gum. "But scraping gum is so rewarding."

Teeny dropped her stack of dirty dishes at the kitchen pass-through and turned to Miss May. "So! What's up?"

"You know what's up," Miss May leaned forward and whispered. "I've got an update."

"Nice!" Teeny smiled and waited for Miss May to spill. "Let's hear it."

Miss May looked at the crowded restaurant. "I was hoping we could talk about it somewhere more private."

"Works for me!" Teeny took me and Miss May by the hands and led us out the front entrance, onto the sidewalk. As soon as we got outside, she turned to us with an excited smile. "All right. Let's hear it!"

I looked back at the line of people inside. "You don't need to be in there?"

"Nah. Granny's got it under control."

I peeked inside. Granny was still sitting motionless behind the counter. *I guess that counts as 'under control'?*

Teeny clapped her hands together. "Come on, then. Out with it already!"

"Well." Miss May tightened her scarf around her neck. "I think we should change our focus. Try to figure out who killed the bookie."

"Smart. I bet whoever was after Vlad knew how to get at that cash." Teeny applied lip balm — vital in the Pine Grove cold — but didn't take her eyes off of Miss May. "Hold up, though. Does that mean you're not going to figure out who killed Charles anymore? Gigley hired you to find out who killed Charles. You need to stick with your original assignment, if you want to build the Thomas Girls Sleuthing Agency brand."

Miss May snatched the lip balm from Teeny and used it herself. "We're not building a brand, Teeny. And even if we were, my theory is that the same person killed both victims. If we find Vlad's killer, I suspect it will lead us to whoever killed Charles."

Teeny gasped and clutched her necklace. "Get out of here! Chelsea, are you hearing this theory!?"

"I heard it last night," I said. "It makes sense."

Teeny rubbed her hands together to warm them up. "So we've got a classic 'two birds, one murderer' situation here."

"It could be." Miss May pulled her gloves off and handed them to Teeny. "Here. My hands are fine."

"May! You are too sweet." Teeny took the gloves and slipped them on. "So what's next?"

"Right," Miss May said. "We figured you might want to tag along for the next part of the investigation."

Teeny erupted with glee. "OK!"

"Like I said," Miss May continued, "if we get more information on the bookie, Vlad, we think it might lead us to the killer."

"So?" Teeny asked.

"So we want go back to Peach and look at her records. But I figured you'd want to accompany us."

"Uh, yeah! Can you wait until it slows down a little here?"

Teeny held the door open as a group of fifteen people entered Grandma's. "My swamp just got a little swampier."

Miss May shook her head. "I don't know. We need to get moving on this investigation."

Teeny stamped her foot. "May! Peach is my sister. You can't go without me. Plus you need me! You catch Peach in the wrong mood, that girl can be tough."

Miss May crossed her arms. "I've known her since before I knew you."

Teeny stood tall. "So you know I'm right!"

Miss May and Teeny looked at one another for a long moment. Then Miss May broke. "Fine. We'll wait. But at least let us help you handle this rush."

Teeny waved us off. "I've got it under control. I need ten, fifteen minutes tops."

"Are you sure? I'm a great helper," I said. "I've been Miss May's sous-chef for years!"

"Don't know what a sous-chef is, but I don't need any more cooks in that kitchen! I'm breaking health codes left and right as it is."

A passing customer gave Teeny a funny look as he entered the restaurant. Teeny held the door for him. "Just kidding! Health department loves me!"

She looked at us and shook her head like, "the health department does not love me."

"Fifteen minutes?" Miss May confirmed.

Teeny darted inside, calling over her shoulder, "Tops!"

As it turned out, Teeny's rush lasted until almost five o'clock that evening. Miss May and I waited the first hour at *Grandma's*. Then Miss May got antsy, so we went back to the orchard to pass the time until Teeny was free.

Once we got back to the orchard, the first thing Miss

May did was meet with KP to plan out next year's crops. Even though it was the dead of winter, Miss May was diligent about prepping for apple-picking season. Last fall the Red Delicious hadn't grown as Miss May had hoped, so she and KP talked about adjusting the soil pH to improve the crops.

I won't say listening to Miss May and KP talk about fertilizing dirt for over an hour bored me, but it wasn't the most interesting conversation I had ever heard. Especially not compared to our investigation, which had gotten me hooked on clues and gossip like they were hard drugs. So I went out to the barn to review the details with our resident tiny horse, See-Saw.

Some people talked to See-Saw in a baby voice, because she was so little and, OK, cute. But I preferred to speak to her in a grown-up voice, like we were chatting over a cup of coffee, or whatever horses drink to perk up. *Horse coffee? Whatever.* See-Saw was a grown woman, so that's how I treated her.

I fed See-Saw some hay when I entered. Then I got down to brass tacks.

"Can you believe we've got another murder on our hands?" I asked. "But this time, there's two bodies. Plus, all that missing money. Miss May got so upset last night. I've never seen her like that."

See-Saw stomped her back leg. I decided it was a supportive gesture.

"Yeah. I guess maybe I'm a little stressed. I try to push that stuff down, but I'm worried. I don't want half of Pine Grove to lose their life savings. And I don't know if I'm helping much."

My throat got all lumpy and tight. I hadn't realized it, but everything I was saying to See-Saw was true. I was full-on stressed. My voice wobbled like an old record as I continued.

"When we solved the first murder, I thought I took good strides, you know? I was bold and brave, and I even drove a car. Took the literal and figurative wheel. Then the theater thing happened, and I got over my stage fright. Kind of."

See-Saw snorted. I fed her more hay.

"I feel stronger now. For sure. But it's still a journey. Like with Jennifer Paul! At the festival. Why did I pay for her donuts? And then agree to have her cut my hair? And why did I let Teeny guilt me into competing in that sled race? Why do I care so much about pleasing other people?"

See-Saw turned away and chewed at her right flank. She had an itch, and she had no patience for this kind of self-indulgence.

"I know. I'm talking about myself too much. What's new with you?"

See-Saw turned back, presumably to open up about her own internal struggles. But Miss May burst into the barn and interrupted.

"There you are, Chelsea! C'mon. Teeny's rush finally died down. It's go-time!"

I laughed. "Go-time?"

"I was trying a thing. Get over it."

Miss May hurried away. I lingered for a moment. Gave See-Saw a nice firm pat on the side of her neck.

"Wish me luck, See-Saw. I'm about to return to the scene of the crime."

See-Saw whinnied, then pooped. I decided it was another gesture of support. Or maybe it was "go-time" for her, too.

19

RESERVATION RUMINATION

*B*y the time Miss May, Teeny, and I walked up to the inn, it was almost four-thirty, and the whole place had a creepy vibe that made me feel unsettled and scared.

The still, gray day had become a windy, gray dusk. Hundred-foot trees rattled. Branches snapped and fell into the pond. Snowdrifts blew off the yard and swirled around us. A forgotten swatch of police tape snagged on a fence post and flapped in the wind.

Miss May stopped and looked around before we climbed the porch. "Spooky out here."

Teeny nodded. "No cars in the lot, either."

"Dead bodies aren't great for business. I know that all too well." Miss May trudged up the steps and opened the door.

I hurried inside, looking forward to the warm, cozy atmosphere that Peach was so good at crafting. But the lobby was even more depressing than the parking lot.

All the lights were off. A sheet hung over the baby grand

piano. A half-drunk cup of tea sat forgotten on an end table, lip-stick stain still visible on the rim.

Teeny crossed to the check-in area. Looked around. Poked her head in the dining room. Came back out to the lobby. "What the heck is going on in here? Why is it so empty?"

Teeny stood on the first step of the staircase and called up. "Peach? Hello?"

"Teeny? What are you doing here?" Peach plodded into the living room, wearing a long floral night gown and eating Chinese food straight out of the container. *A move I knew all too well.*

Teeny jumped off the stair and hurried to Peach. "Peach! What's going on here? You closed for the winter or something?"

Peach took a big, somber bite of lo mein. Chewed. Swallowed. "Everyone checked out the day the dead body showed up. Said the dead guy was haunting the place."

Teeny scoffed. "That's ridiculous! He didn't even die inside."

"That's what I said." Peach let out a little burp. "People didn't seem to care about the semantics." Peach plopped down in one of her floral armchairs. "I didn't invest with that Fitz kid, so I thought I'd get out of this unscathed. Turns out I was wrong."

I ran my hand across the covered piano. "You haven't had any new bookings?"

Peach shook her head. "Someone posted about the body in an online review. I got on there. Issued a forceful reply. Had words. Turns out the more your type 'No one is haunting my inn!' in all caps, the more people think you've got a haunted inn."

"Oh no," I said.

"Oh yes." Peach picked up the receiver on the phone and slammed it down. "Might as well disconnect this damn thing."

"People don't like hanging around a crime scene," Miss May said. "Same thing happened at the orchard. We were slow for almost a month after the murder. But once we solved it, and the Gazette reported it wasn't our fault, people came back."

Peach looked at the eerie scene out the window. "So you've got to solve this one too, then. For the sake of my business."

"That's why we're here." Teeny pulled Peach out of the chair. "Come on. We need to see your records."

When Peach opened the door to her office, three boxes, a toaster, and a tea kettle spilled into the hall.

Peach kicked the boxes away and stepped inside. "Pardon the mess."

"Mess" was a generous word for what most people would categorize as a FEMA-level disaster. I could not see a single square inch of Peach's office floor. Nor could I see a single square inch of the surface of Peach's desk. Nor could I spot her computer, her keyboard, or anywhere she might have had records that could have been useful to our investigation.

Papers, folders, binders and notepads blocked the floor. Enormous sleeves of plastic cups leaned against the window like so many towers of Pisa. Cookie sheets and baking supplies blocked the entrance to the closet. Cute stuffed cows topped every surface, like somehow Peach thought adding a few Holsteins hid the clutter.

Teeny moved a broken old fax machine onto the floor, which revealed a sliver of a puffy, floral couch. She sat down and took everything in. "Peach. If your guests saw this—"

"One of them did," Peach said. "Wrote about it on several stupid Internet review sites."

Miss May stayed focused on the task at hand. "Do you think the records might be on a computer or something?"

"I do, May. Thank you for the brilliant idea. Too bad I have no clue where that damn machine is." Peach shuffled papers around on her desk. "I hate that damn laptop! The desktop was impossible to lose. It was always on top of the desk!"

Peach got down on her hands and knees, moved what appeared to be a badminton set, and looked under the couch. "Not under here."

"What about print-outs?" I asked. "Or a guest book? Do you have your guests sign in? Anything like that?"

"Nope," Peach said. "We're going to need to find that computer if I'm going to help you at all."

OK, not to honk my own horn, but I happened to be the best person at finding lost things on the face of the planet. I first realized I had the skill in elementary school, when I found Judd Anderson's missing retainer all the way at the bottom of the dumpster. After that, I became the go-to girl whenever anyone lost anything. Yes, usually it was retainers, and that was gross. But I had also located several missing cats, and even a pet turtle. As an adult, I once stayed at a bar until four in the morning to help a stranger find her keys. When I finally found them, she had already called a lock-smith. But I didn't care. I had solved the case of the missing keys, and it had felt good.

As Peach crawled around her office looking for her laptop, I wanted to help. But I also didn't want to make her feel bad about the mess. Any other day, my fear of stepping on Peach's toes would have won out. But I had just talked to See-Saw about being less of a people-pleaser. So I got on the floor and crawled around right beside Peach.

"I can find it," I said. "I'm great at finding missing stuff."

"She certainly is." Miss May cleared another spot on the couch and plopped down. "Found at least four hundred retainers in elementary school."

Most people think that the secret to finding lost things is "re-tracing your steps." That helps. But it's not too helpful in situations like the one we were in, where you're looking for something on someone else's behalf. So instead, I liked to focus on the minute details of the search, just like I would with my interior design.

Finding something required a sharp eye, but not just for the object itself. Any lamp out of place, any crooked photo on the wall, any couch cushion slightly askew could be a clue. When I really hunkered down to find a lost item, I treated the whole room as a puzzle and the item as the missing piece.

This strategy was harder in Peach's office. I'd scoured dumpsters that were more organized.

My big breakthrough came when I realized we shouldn't be looking on the floor. Even Peach wouldn't leave something as valuable as a laptop lying around waiting to be stepped on. Also, Peach needed to access the computer too often to cover it up with papers on the desk. So I took to the high ground and climbed onto a chair to get a bird's-eye view.

Et voila! The laptop rested atop the bookshelf, which was the only clear surface in the room.

"I found it!" I smiled. "On top of the bookshelf!"

Peach reached up — she'd gotten the tall genes in

Teeny's family — and grabbed the laptop. "I always put it there, and I never remember! Thank you, Chelsea."

I grabbed Miss May's shoulder to steady myself and climbed off the chair. "It's what I do." It was hard not to sound too self-satisfied, so I let it ride. "They didn't call me the 'Patron Saint of Lost Retainers' for nothing."

"That's a weird nickname." Peach opened the laptop. "Did the other kids really call you that?"

"Some of them did." I flushed. "But mostly, it was just me. In my head."

Peach scoffed, then started up the computer. The device took a few minutes to boot up, and when it finally turned on, I gasped.

The virtual desktop was even more cluttered than Peach's real desktop. There were a thousand little icons and files, stacked every which way. And there didn't seem to be rhyme or reason to any of it.

Teeny groaned. "Peach! What's with the files?"

"I know it looks bad." Peach clicked around. "But I have a system."

Teeny straightened the books on Peach's shelf. "Hope it's not the same system you use to keep track of your things."

"It's not." Peach click-clicked, and a few seconds later, a document popped up on screen. "Here are all my reservations for the past six months." Peach stood and slogged toward the room's exit. "If you need me, I'll be in my chair, eating my noodles."

Miss May called after Peach. "Thank you, Peach!"

Peach grunted and shuffled out.

Then Miss May cleared a little space and sat down at the computer. "Now let's take a look at this reservation file." She scrolled through Peach's spreadsheet. "Wow. It's...meticulous. She's got names, addresses, room numbers. She even has a little section with notes on each guest. 'Loves the color blue.' 'Puts cinnamon in coffee.' No wonder people love this place."

Teeny smiled, proud. "Hospitality runs in the family, I guess." She scooted to the edge of the couch. "Any notes on our guy? Vlad?"

Miss May kept scrolling. "Getting there, getting there... Ah! Here he is. But... what the heck?"

"What's wrong?" I asked.

"Peach has a full write-up on every customer who's been in here since summer. But for this guy, it only says 'Vlad.' No last name. No credit card number. No cinnamon in his coffee."

"That can't be right." I circled behind Miss May, commandeered the mouse and clicked around. Miss May was not mistaken. The only information on Vlad was his first name. Not even a last initial. "Wow. That's really it," I conceded.

"Well, that's a dead end then. Maybe we should go ask Peach if she remembers anything else," Teeny stood and turned to leave, but Miss May remained fixated on the computer.

"Hold on a sec," Miss May said. "Let's see who else was staying here around that time." She scrolled one line at a time. "Don't know them. Don't know them. Don't know them. Wait!" Miss May sat bolt upright, then turned to me and Teeny, eyes wide. "Florence Fitz booked a room here last month."

Teeny rushed to look at the laptop. There it was, in black and white. *Florence Fitz.* "That's weird. Who stays at a BnB in their own town?" Teeny frowned.

"That's a thing now," I said. "It's called a stay-cation."

"But why would I want to stay in Pine Grove when I

could go to Barbuda?" Teeny held up her hands in confusion.

"Will you two hush up? I'm investigating here." Miss May moved from column to column, looking for more information on Florence Fitz. "It says here she requested two cups of coffee."

"Maybe Charles was with her."

"That's true." Miss May looked up at me. "Or..."

I inspected the file. "Or she was with another guy?"

"Not sure." Miss May snapped the laptop closed and stood up. "But we're going to find out."

20

NOODLES OF CLUES

Once we extricated ourselves from the back office, we asked Peach about Florence's summer visit to the inn. Peach answered without looking up from her cup of noodles.

"When she checked in, she was by herself."

Miss May sat on the chair beside Peach. "So she stayed here alone all weekend?"

Peach looked up with half-chewed noodle in her mouth. "I said she checked in alone." Peach slurped down the noodle and got to work selecting her next bite. "I thought I heard her talking to someone in her room that night. I assumed it was Charles."

"Makes sense." Miss May looked out the window. "Did she stay here often over the years?"

"You mean like for a stay-cation?" Peach cracked open a soda and took a sip. "Nope. Last month was the first time she booked a room here. Ever."

"And you can't say for certain who she was with?"

"I'd rather not repeat myself, May. If you haven't noticed, I've got noodles to eat!"

"And they look delicious," Miss May said. "It's just... If Flo were with Charles, it could be normal. And if she was with another man...well, that's more suspicious."

Peach slammed her cup of noodles down on the table. "Are you done here? Good. I'd like to stop discussing murder at my inn."

Miss May pressed on. "Actually, I was also wondering if you had any more information on the dead guy. Your file only has his first name, 'Vlad,' but every other guest has a ton of information."

"Do you think it's possible that his first name is the only information he shared, May? Could that perhaps have something to do with the fact that he was a rotten crook? Have you considered that the man who turned up dead in my rose bush didn't pull me into the sitting room for a fireside chat?"

Teeny glared at her sister. "Peach. Be nice!"

"No, Teeny," Miss May said. "She's right. I'm asking stupid questions." Miss May half-bowed to Peach in apology. "We'll see ourselves out."

"See yourself over to the trash first." Peach handed Miss May the now-empty cup of noodles. "I'm done here."

By the time we left the inn, night had fallen. Hard. There was a new moon that night, so Pine Grove was pitch black, and the spooky vibes I had gotten earlier had turned full-on creepy.

The sounds of the night were like a "Greatest Hits" album of ominous ambient noise.

Howling wind? Check. Random whistling sound? Check. Branches snapping? Check. Sirens in the distance?

Check. The sound of a crying baby, abandoned somewhere in its bassinet? I swear I heard that too.

My chest got all squishy with fear, but Miss May didn't seem to notice the creepy noises at all. Even if she did, she and Teeny were way too deep in problem-solving mode to bother with nerves.

"We need more clues." Miss May kicked a pinecone as she walked.

Teeny kicked the pinecone a little further ahead. "Hey. Peach tried!"

Miss May scoffed, and Teeny glared at her. I tried to keep the conversation on track. "At least we gained a little information," I said. "Florence Fitz stayed at the *Dragonfly* a month ago."

"I guess," Miss May said. "But I'm frustrated. Tom Gigley hired me for a job, and I'm not getting it done."

"It's not my sister's fault!" Teeny pouted.

"Will you stop, Teeny? I never said it was Peach's fault."

"Stop yelling at me!"

"I'm not yelling! You are!"

Truth is, they were both yelling. So I tried to smooth things over with an idea.

"Maybe we should sleep on it," I said. "A theory might pop into one of our heads tomorrow. How about we reconvene at *Grandma's* in the morning to talk it over?"

"*Grandma's* is closed tomorrow morning for Charles Fitz's wake," Teeny said. "We'll open after, so everyone can come by and talk about the guy like he was some kind of saint."

"Teeny!" Miss May said.

"Sorry. May he rest in peace. I'm just annoyed."

"What if we use the wake as a fact-finding mission?" I asked. "If we go, we can suss out whether Charles was with

Florence at the hotel that weekend. And if he wasn't, perhaps we can figure out who was?"

Miss May stopped walking. "Actually...that's a great idea."

Teeny and I replied in unison. "It is?"

"I'm not saying it's the most respectful plan. But everyone in town will be at that wake. All we have to do is find the right person and get them talking."

Teeny scrunched up her face. "I don't know. It's the man's funeral. Even if he wasn't a saint..."

"I hear you, Teeny," Miss May said. "And under normal circumstances, I would agree. But if we don't sort this out, someone else might turn up dead. Soon. So investigating at the wake, in some ways, is the most considerate thing we can do."

"That's a good point," Teeny kicked another pinecone. "The killer is still out there. Someone else could die at any moment."

"So," Miss May said. "What do you think?"

"I think Chelsea needs a nice black dress for tomorrow," Teeny said. "Do you have one, or do you want to borrow one of mine?"

When we arrived at the wake, I expected attendance to be sparse. But as we walked up to the funeral home, I realized I had been wrong. The entire town was in attendance. Whether or not Fitz owed them money, they were all there. And it seemed like they all wanted to pay genuine respects.

I straightened the too-tight dress I had borrowed from Teeny. "Look at all these people. It's like the death of a rockstar or something."

Miss May took my elbow as we walked. "You haven't been to a funeral in Pine Grove in too long." Miss May let out a deep sigh. "I doubt you remember. But when your parents..."

"It was packed," I said. *That was a hard day to forget.* "But was it more packed than this?"

"Ten times." Miss May squeezed my arm. "People couldn't stop talking about how beautiful you were. Just like your mother."

Miss May almost never talked about her sister. *My mom.* But when she did, she got this look in her eyes that was simultaneously faraway and intimate. Like we were the only two people in the entire world who understood that life is fleeting but beautiful. And that anything with the power to make you happy might one day also make you sad.

Whewph! I was not in the mood to think deep thoughts that day, and Miss May's mention of my mom was about as much as I could handle. So I shook the feelings off like a big, wet dog and motioned toward the door to the funeral home.

"Should we go in? See what we can find out?"

Miss May nodded. "Just remember to be respectful."

21

ASSAULT AND ARREST

*W*hen we entered the wake, my mind flooded with memories of my parents' funeral almost twenty years prior. The place hadn't changed one bit. Same plum-red carpets. Same simple wooden chairs. Same peaceful paintings of gardens and sunsets and other metaphors for endings and new beginnings.

It took everything I had not to turn around and run down the street bawling. But I had a job to do... solve the murder of the guy in the coffin. So I looked around, on the hunt for clues.

I started by taking a mental note of everyone in the room. Brian from the *Brown Cow* was kneeling at the coffin. Vice Principal Frank sat alone in the back row of chairs, head bowed in respect. Miss May and Teeny were standing along the far wall. Principal Fitz stood up front, accepting condolences from mourners. And Liz was badgering Mayor Delgado near the exit.

As I watched Liz, I almost laughed out loud. I should have known that Miss May and I would not be the only people investigating at this funeral. Liz was gunning for whatever Pine Grove's equivalent of a Pulitzer was, and she was clearly hassling the mayor for an interview about something. She didn't seem to care all that much about showing respect for the dead.

That's when it hit me. There was no way Miss May would get any valuable information at this wake. And there was no way Miss May would seriously question any of the mourners, either. It was a plan that had sounded decent in theory, but in practice? Funeral sleuthing was not our style. Not even a little.

I waited off to the side as Miss May and Teeny kneeled and said a prayer in the front of the room. When they stood and crossed to me, I could tell they felt the same way I did.

"We're not talking to anyone at this funeral." Miss May folded up a prayer card and put it in her pocket. "It's not right."

"I know," I said.

Miss May cast a look over at Liz, who was still questioning the mayor across the room. Miss May clucked her tongue and said, "I do, however, know how we might get the information we need."

"Liz!" Miss May hurried across the parking lot to catch up with the departing reporter. "Can we talk?"

"Can't. Sorry." Liz unlocked her car. "I'm on the cusp of something here."

"So are we."

Liz pulled her notepad out of her bag. "Are you willing to go on the record for this conversation?"

"What? No! We don't want you to interview us. We want access to your information."

Liz shook her head. "I heard the three of you were running around playing detective. That's against the law, you know. I think you should give me something I can use in my story, so I don't have to run and tell the cops about your sleuthing."

Miss May laughed. "You will not bribe me, Elizabeth. Because if you do, I will tell your mother. And she did not raise an extortionist."

Liz shrugged. "Fine. Tell my mom. See if I care."

Liz opened the door to her car. Miss May caught her by the shoulder.

"Wait!"

Liz turned back with a sly smirk. "I thought you might change your tune."

"You probably already know everything we know," Miss May said.

"Try me."

"You know the guy who showed up dead at the inn worked in politics?"

"Of course." Liz scribbled something in her pad.

Teeny looked over at me. "Politics," she mouthed, confused.

"Just go with it," I said. Miss May was lying about Vlad's identity to help our investigation, and Liz was playing right into the ruse.

"So you're also aware that the guy had travelled up from Brooklyn to try to get Charles to fund his campaign." Miss May sounded so sure of herself, I almost believed her alternate facts.

Liz scoffed. "Yes, May."

I stepped forward, eager to join in the ploy. "Then maybe you know the one thing we don't know."

Liz turned to face me. "And what's that, Chelsea?"

"Why was Florence Fitz staying at the *Dragonfly Inn* last month?" I was so proud of myself for asking the right question at the right time, I spoke my next sentence as loud and clear as I could. "Because I think she was having an affair."

A shriek sounded from behind us, and I turned to see Florence Fitz, my former high school principal, charging toward me from the funeral home.

"Chelsea Thomas! How dare you!?"

I stammered. "Uh, sorry. Did you hear that? I didn't mean—"

Florence smacked me with her purse. I tried to fend her off, but she kept right on smacking. "I cannot believe you are gossiping about me at Charles' wake. What is wrong with you!?"

Florence pulled her purse back to take another swing, but Miss May and Teeny grabbed Principal Fitz's arms and pulled her away.

"Florence! Calm down!" Miss May said.

"Get off me, Mabel!"

Florence grappled with Miss May and shoved my aunt away. The frazzled principal spun around and noticed a dozen mourners gathered in the parking lot, watching the ordeal.

"What are you all looking at!?" Florence said. "The crazy, sad widow, losing her mind for no good reason? I'll show you no good reason. These harlots are out here gossiping about me."

I muttered another apology, but Miss May hushed me and stepped toward Principal Fitz. "Florence. Let me explain. We—"

"No, let me explain." Florence glared at me as she spoke. "Charles and I stayed at the *Dragonfly* last month to celebrate our anniversary. Does that answer your question,

Chelsea? Or should I go on? Should I tell you about the love I felt for him? How I'll treasure that weekend forever? Would you like me to go into detail about how those few days were precious, and I only wish I had realized it at the time?"

Detective Wayne Hudson hurried out of the funeral home. "Mrs. Fitz. Is everything OK here?"

"Everything is not OK, Detective. This girl is disturbing the peace at my husband's wake!"

Wayne looked over at me. "What girl? Chelsea?"

"Yes. Chelsea Thomas," Principal Fitz shrieked. "I would like her arrested."

I gasped. "What!?" I couldn't believe it. *My former principal was demanding my arrest?* This was a nightmare come true.

"That's right, you heartless monster," Florence hissed. "I want you in jail. For life."

Wayne looked from me, then back to Florence, then back to me. "Uh... I'm not sure this situation calls for an arrest. But Chelsea, why don't you come down to the station for...some questioning?"

"That's it?" Florence said. "You're taking it easy on her!"

Wayne adjusted his jacket. "We'll proceed as necessary from there." He looked at me. "OK?"

I got the impression that Wayne wanted me to say yes to resolve the conflict as soon as possible, so I obliged.

"OK. Sure. I'm sorry, Principal Fitz."

"No," Florence said. "I want her arrested!"

"I understand that, Mrs. Fitz. Don't you worry, I'm taking care of this." Wayne turned back toward the crowd of people. "Can someone help Mrs. Fitz back inside? Thank you."

Brian hurried over and walked Mrs. Fitz back in to the

funeral home. Mrs. Fitz called over her shoulder at me, "You should be ashamed of yourself, Ms. Thomas."

"I'm sorry," I said again.

"We're all sorry, Florence." Miss May held her hands over her heart. "You're right to be mad."

Mrs. Fitz shook her head and disappeared inside the funeral home with Brian and the other mourners. I felt the pressure of a thousand eyes burning into my face, even though no one was looking at me anymore. *This was going to take a long time to live down.*

I'd reacted in self-defense to being purse-smacked, but once the adrenaline subsided, the shame of what I'd done settled into my bones and stayed there. Gossiping with Liz in the parking lot of the funeral was no better than questioning people inside the funeral home itself.

Worst of all, we didn't even get to ask Liz a single question. We still had no clue why she was so interested in the mayor, for instance. Plus, our hunch about Principal Fitz at the *Dragonfly* had been a red herring. Mr. and Mrs. Fitz were on a stay-cation, after all.

Wayne's gruff baritone snapped me back to the present. "All right, Chelsea. Let's go."

Oh right. I have to go the station. Wayne took me by the arm and led me over to his unmarked cruiser.

Miss May stepped between us and the car. "Hold on a second! Is she being placed under arrest?"

Wayne shook his head. "No one is being placed under arrest. We're just going to talk."

"So it's more like a date then," Miss May said with a smug grin. *Groan.* "In that case. I'll see you both down at the station."

"It's not a... she's not... this isn't... Chelsea can ride with you if she wants," Wayne said. I glanced up at him. Detective

Hudson was not a man easy to fluster, yet my aunt had accomplished the feat with the mere mention of a date. *Hmmm.*

Teeny waved Wayne off. "May's backseat is broken. And I'm riding up front. Sorry. Chelsea's got to ride right beside you. All alone. In that romantic little undercover car."

I flushed bright red. This awkwardness was more humiliating than being beaten with my principal's purse. I wheeled on Teeny and Miss May. "Will you two stop?" Then I smiled up at Wayne and tossed my hair, doing my best impression of a confident woman. "I'm sorry. They're being silly."

"It's fine." Wayne sounded a little nervous, and he cleared his throat. "But uh, you need to ride in the back. For legal reasons."

"Not a problem," I said. Wayne opened the back door to the car, and I climbed in.

22

DETECTIVES AND DIALOGUE

*R*iding in the back of Wayne's cramped squad car was the opposite of romantic. Could have been because of the thick slab of bulletproof glass between us. Or because I was still reeling from my encounter with the Widow Fitz. *Hell hath no fury like a principal scorned*, I thought with a shudder.

Once Wayne and I got to the jail, the whole afternoon took a surprisingly pleasant turn. We entered the station to find a single, scrawny deputy stuffing envelopes. I recognized the deputy as my nervous guard from the night of the sled-race. Otherwise, the place was emptier than my Jersey City fridge.

"Where is everyone?" I asked.

"Softball game. Police versus Fire Department."

"You didn't want to play?"

"Two murders this close together? I'd rather catch bad guys than softballs."

I stifled a laugh. Wayne glanced at me. "What? That makes you laugh?"

"I mean, yeah. You'd rather 'catch bad guys than soft-balls?' That sounds kinda silly."

Wayne half-smiled but buried his amusement with a cough. "Not silly. True." Wayne nodded toward a desk along the window. "Take a seat. You want anything?"

An invitation to a nice dinner? A glass of decent red wine? A lingering hug? The list went on... "I guess I'd kind of like to know what I'm doing here, if I'm not under arrest."

"I had to do something back there. Mrs. Fitz was upset. Understandably." Wayne handed me a can of soda, sat down, and cracked a can of his own. "First her husband gets killed. Now she has to deal with people questioning her fidelity at his funeral?"

"I wasn't just going around yelling that she was a cheater. I tried to to be discreet."

"A swing and a miss," Wayne said.

"I thought you weren't a softball guy," I retorted. *Where did I get the gall to talk to a policeman like this?* Something about Detective Wayne Hudson drew out my snark. I liked it.

Wayne chuckled. "Just because I prefer police work to team sports doesn't mean I can't pull a solid baseball reference now and then. I'm familiar with America's pastime."

"Ugh, I bet you're one of those guys who was good at every sport in high school." *Unlike me.*

Wayne offered a shrug and a coy smirk in response, which was a clear confirmation that I was right. "What makes you say that?"

Uh, you're a beefy hunk of a man with quick reflexes and a ton of confidence? "I don't know," I said. "I guess you just have that vibe. Not a jock vibe, but like a...competent vibe."

"Competent, wow. What a compliment."

"Coming from me, it is! I was so incompetent in gym class that I got the nickname 'Racket Face.'"

Wayne looked confused. I clarified, "Oh, well I was particularly sucky at tennis. So much so that the gym teacher would say, 'Chelsea, you're supposed to hit the ball with the racket, not your face!' Hence the nickname."

"That's rough," Wayne said, with genuine sympathy. "I'm glad those tennis balls didn't inflict permanent damage."

Oh my goodness, Wayne was staring at my face. Hard. As if... he liked what he saw. Well, time for me to shove my foot firmly into my mouth. "You don't think I have a dented face?" I asked.

"A dented face? No. Your face looks great to me." *GAAAAHHHHHH. Keep it together, Chelsea.*

"Oh. Cool, cool. Yep. Your face is also not dented." I swallowed a sip of soda and it went down the wrong pipe. I immediately gurgled and coughed so forcefully that Wayne jumped to his feet.

"Are you OK, Chelsea? Can you give me a thumbs up for OK?"

I weakly raised my thumb and tried not to spit all over myself. I choked out the words, "Wrong pipe." Wayne started to laugh. I narrowed my eyes at him. "Not funny!"

"You look like a cat with a hairball," Wayne snickered. "A cute cat, though. One of those fuzzy white ones or whatever."

"A Persian?" I sputtered.

"Sure, that," he said. The cough travelled into my nose and I sneezed. Wayne offered me a tissue. "Here. Gesundheit."

"Thanks." Our fingers brushed as I took the tissue from him. A sizzle of electricity raced up my arm, leaving a trail of warmth that made me want to keep touching Wayne's hand.

Did Wayne feel that too? Maybe! I was feeling emboldened and I reached out, about to graze Wayne's arm...but then I sneezed again, and I had to cover my mouth instead. *RIP Romantic Moment.*

"Look, Chelsea, I just want to say...I know you're trying to help, asking around about Charles Fitz. I know your aunt had a lot of money with him. But you could get really hurt if you keep poking around like this. And I'm not just talking getting smacked around with a lady's purse, either."

"Who's poking around?" I took a sip of my soda. It went down smooth this time.

"At first I thought it was just your aunt snooping around and you were tagging along for the ride," Wayne said. "But I'm starting to think you're the real snoop."

"Am not," I said.

"You sure about that?" Wayne asked.

To tell or not to tell? Gigley had warned me and Miss May not to trust the police when this much money was involved. But I had no reason to believe Wayne or any Pine Grove cop was corrupt.

"Are you thinking about whether or not you can trust the cops?"

I almost jumped out of my skin. "No. Trust the cops with what? I don't know anything." *I guess I'm keeping the investigation secret.*

Wayne jabbed his thumb toward Main Street. "You see those people out there?"

"What people?" I asked. I looked out the window, but I saw zero people. "There's no one out there."

Wayne harrumphed and snapped the blinds closed. "You know, 'the people.' The general population of Pine Grove. They pay taxes to keep this station open. They trust us. Everyone in this town does. Except for you and your aunt, apparently."

I shrugged. "Those taxes also pay for softball games?"

"You think you're funny?" *Kind of.* Wayne shook his head. "There are bad people involved with this thing."

"What do you mean? The bookie? Is someone else involved?" Sure, Vlad had not been not an upstanding citizen. But he was dead. *Did Wayne have information we didn't have? Was someone even more dangerous than Vlad involved in these murders?*

"There's still a murderer on the loose." Wayne cracked his knuckles. "Isn't there?"

I crossed my arms. "You tell me."

Wayne scoffed.

"I'm serious," I said. "Maybe I can help."

"Help how? You're an interior decorator. Your aunt owns an apple orchard. You guys bake cookies for a living."

Wayne wasn't wrong, but my ears flamed with annoyance. His tone was patronizing, and I didn't like it. I sat up a little straighter. "That's a diminutive assessment of what we do." *Also, technically I was an unemployed interior designer, but that didn't seem worth a mention.*

"Stop the damn sleuthing, Chelsea. For real."

"We solved the last murder," I mumbled. "We figured out who killed Vinny."

"Yeah, and I would've too. Except that some busybodies kept interfering."

"We're not busybodies."

Wayne pushed his chair back and stood up. "You're free to go."

"Detective Hudson. Wayne," I said. "I thought we were having a conversation. Now you're kicking me out?"

"I'm not kicking you out," Wayne pointed toward the door. "Your aunt and her friend just got here."

I turned.

Miss May gave a little wave from the doorway. "Hope we're not interrupting."

"You're not," Wayne said.

You are, I thought.

"Are you sure?" Miss May winked at us.

Teeny smothered her girlish giggle in her hand. My face blushed redder than a Red Delicious.

Miss May's voice shifted from meddling aunt to stern lawyer. "So. What's the meaning of this anyway? It's not every day you see a detective detain an innocent citizen for no reason whatsoever."

Wayne balked. "There was a grieving widow—"

"One grieving widow and all proper police procedure goes out the door?"

"It's fine," I said. "We already talked about it. Wayne was just placating Principal Fitz. Right?"

"That's an oversimplification of my duties, but essentially," Wayne said.

"Well, as long as you two worked it out," Miss May said. "Sorry we took so long to get here. The line at Brian's was out the door." Miss May handed Wayne a cup from the *Brown Cow.* "Latte?"

"I don't do lattes." Wayne's hackles were up. Miss May could have offered him a straight shot of bootleg whiskey, and it wouldn't have been manly enough for him.

"You know a latte is just coffee and milk, right?" Teeny sipped her drink. "And it is oh so delicious!"

"You're kind of looking a gift latte in the mouth," I said. I was feeling pugnacious toward Wayne, and his rejection of Miss May's generosity rankled me.

Wayne sighed. "OK. I'll take the stupid foamy thing. Thank you. So much."

Wayne grabbed the latte from his desk and I watched as he took a sip. He clearly liked the drink and he glanced my way with a grudging smile. I smiled back. I wasn't sure why we were smiling, but I liked it. *I liked it a lot.*

When we left the station, Miss May threw her arm around my shoulders.

"Alright, jailbird. What do you want for dinner? Anywhere you want to go."

I looked over at Teeny with a sly smile, and she read my mind. "She wants HBL!"

"What's HBL?" Miss May asked.

Teeny and I replied in unison. "Hashbrown Lasagna!"

Half an hour later, we were sitting in our usual booth at *Grandma's,* reviewing the case in between bites of HBL.

Teeny licked her fork. "That is soooooooooo good!" She never shied away from complimenting her own creations. "I see a Michelin star in my future." Teeny glanced at Miss May's barely touched plate. "What's the matter? Was yours not good?"

Miss May pushed the cheesy masterpiece around on her plate. "No, no. It was good. Of course it was."

Teeny stole a bit of Miss May's food. "So what's wrong?"

"Nothing. Everything's fine. It's just..." Miss May looked up at Teeny. "I should have known better than to suspect Florence. She's a friend. And we went to her husband's funeral and —"

"We didn't actually question anyone," Teeny said.

"But we almost did," Miss May said.

"Think of it this way," Teeny said. "If we had solved the crime at the funeral, I think it would have been worth it. Right?"

Miss May shrugged. "I guess."

"Oh, you know it would have," Teeny said. "And Florence would have been happy, too. Maybe not 'happy' happy. But you know what I mean."

"I guess you're right," Miss May said. "And even if you're not, sitting here and moping doesn't do us much good."

Miss May took a bite of her food, and we sat in silence as she chewed.

"So what's next?" I asked.

Miss May shrugged. "I have no idea."

Yet again, it seemed we were at an impasse.

The bells above the door jangled, and Jennifer Paul entered the restaurant. She was...a touch overdressed for the diner. She wore a floor-length silk dress, and her curly hair was piled on her head in an elegant bun.

I gestured toward Jennifer. "I think she's in the wrong place. Broadway is about fifty miles south."

Teeny chuckled. "*Grandma's* is a classy establishment, but not that classy."

Jennifer slid into a booth across the room. I swiveled my gaze to Miss May. "Maybe our next lead just sat down?"

Miss May frowned. "No way, no how. There's no way I'm questioning another friend in this murder. I messed up enough already."

"Friend?" I raised my eyebrows.

"Chels, I know you don't like the girl, but she's been cutting my hair for almost ten years. Maybe that's not a friend, but it's something."

"She does a great job," Teeny said.

"I have easy hair," Miss May replied.

"Your hair does look great. But your hairdresser was sleeping with the victim," I said. "And look at her clothes. Look at her purse! She clearly just came into money."

Jennifer rifled through a pebbled-leather bucket bag. It was a deep, warm brown with impeccable hand-stitching and a bronze clasp. The thing had "designer brand" written all over it.

"It's a purse, not a Porsche," Miss May said. "She probably got it secondhand or online."

Before I could respond, Liz approached our booth. Dark sunglasses obscured her eyes, despite the encroaching dusk.

"Hello, Teeny. I would like to make an order." Liz spoke in a weird, loud monotone.

"Why are you telling me?" Teeny asked. "I'm off-duty. Also, why are you talking so loud?"

Liz leaned in and hissed, "Act like we're having a casual conversation."

Teeny wiped her mouth. "We are having a casual conversation."

Liz raised her voice again. "Yes, please! One hashbrown lasagna to go. Can you do that extra crispy?"

Teeny looked at me, then back up at Liz. "OK. I'm confused."

I tried to keep a straight face. Teeny wasn't great at picking up on subtlety, and Liz wasn't great at dispensing it.

"I have information," Liz said. "It's all in the note."

"What note?" Teeny asked. "What's going on?"

Liz grabbed Teeny's hand and shook it. "Thank you in advance for the crispy hashbrowns. I love them nice and crispy!"

In a flourish, Liz bustled toward the door and exited as quickly as she'd appeared.

"That was bizarre," Miss May said.

Teeny held up a small piece of paper. "She put a note in my hand!"

"Read it!" Miss May and I said at the same time.

Teeny unfolded the note and whisper-read, "'Pine Grove Dam. Twenty minutes. I know who killed the money man.'"

23

DAMMED IF WE DO

*E*ighteen minutes later, we pulled into the parking lot at Pine Grove Dam. For the second time in a few days, I was revisiting the site of my ill-fated proposal. *Why did Mike have to ruin this scenic spot for me?*

I tried to shake off my bad deja-vu. *I can wallow later*, I reasoned. *At home. Over a large, large plate of cookies. And maybe a donut. I'll play it by ear.*

A few feet away, Liz paced like a caged reporter, still wearing her sunglasses. *Is she hiding something behind those shades?* I wondered. *Or is she losing it under the pressure of the job?*

"Finally!" Liz said as we piled out of the VW bus. "I was beginning to think they'd gotten to you."

They who? I doubted that Liz had solved both murders, but I was curious to hear her theory.

"Calm down, Liz," Miss May said. "Stop pacing and talk to us."

"I don't need to talk. I need to show you something."

Miss May glanced at me, then back to Liz. "OK. What've you got?"

Liz extracted a manila envelope from her purse and handed it to Miss May.

Miss May pinched together the prongs of the envelope and emptied its contents. I peered over her shoulder as she shuffled through several grainy pictures. The photos all showed a woman and a man huddled together under the local Metro north train tracks. The couple looked conspiratorial, like they were sharing state secrets. A lot like how we must have looked in the freezing cold out by the dam.

"Who are those people?" Teeny asked.

Miss May used the flashlight on her phone to get a better look. "I'm not sure. I think the woman might be...the mayor?"

"You bet your shorts that's the mayor," Liz said. "You want to know who she's with?"

"Why else would we be out here freezing our petunias off?" Teeny asked. "Spit it out already!"

"Hey!" Liz bristled. "If you don't like my style, you can leave."

"If this has something to do with the killer, sooner is better than later." Miss May shot a look at Teeny. "I'm sure that's all Teeny is saying."

"Right," Teeny muttered. "So sorry. Didn't mean to offend you. But my petunia is freezing, so..."

"OK. I'm leaving." Liz turned to go.

"Wait," Miss May said.

Liz paused.

Miss May took a steadying breath. "We're all here to figure out who the killer is, right?"

"I guess that's true," Liz said.

"So will you tell us who that man is, and why the photos are so important?" Miss May smiled.

"Fine," Liz said. "The man in the photo is none other than…" *Drumroll, please…* "Vlad."

I blinked. "Vlad, like…dead Vlad?"

"Yup." Liz pointed at the photo. "See? He's wearing the hat from the *Dragonfly*."

Miss May squinted. "Huh. What did he want with the mayor?"

"My suspicion is that the mayor is planning a run at the governor's mansion," Liz said. "But Charles had information that could have compromised her candidacy. So she hired Vlad to kill Charles. I pieced it all together after you confirmed that Vlad was involved in politics. I think Vlad must have been some kind of 'eraser' that people in power use to make things go away."

At first, I thought Liz had to be wrong. Miss May and I had already decided Vlad was a bookie, and we had purposely misdirected Liz toward politics. Still, it was odd that Vlad had been conspiring with the mayor. *What could they have been talking about?*

"Have you told the police about this?" Miss May asked.

Liz shook her head. "I want to break the story in the paper or sell it to the Times. But the mayor hates me, so I haven't been able to get close enough to her to gather more information."

"And that's why you brought this to us," Miss May said.

"You catch on quick," Liz said. "I was hoping now that you have the information, you might do some digging for me."

"What's in it for us?" Teeny asked.

"You get to put another bad guy behind bars," Liz said. "Isn't that what you want?"

Miss May nodded. "That is what we want. You're right." Teeny shrugged like, "more or less."

"So?" Liz looked hopeful. "Are you in?"

Miss May held her hand out.

"Let me see that picture again."

24

RAISING THE STAKEOUTS

The next morning, I prepared for my first official stakeout. The only problem? I had no idea how to prepare for a stakeout. I decided to go with the classic trench coat and sunglasses. I then took an embarrassing "detective selfie," which I immediately deleted from existence. *I did look cute in a trench coat though.*

Miss May decided to take KP's beater rather than her trusty van. "Sunshine yellow" is not an incognito color. And "VW bus" is not an incognito vehicle.

"KP doesn't care if we borrow his car?" I asked.

"I don't know," Miss May said. "I didn't ask him."

"Miss May!"

KP's old junker was Frankensteined together from bits and pieces of other cars. By most standards, it was a monster. But, like any mad doctor, KP loved his creation. And he rarely let anyone else drive it.

Fortunately, Miss May had a spare key, so we piled into the beater with all our stakeout gear. Then we rumbled away from the farm, fingers crossed that KP was too busy feeding See-Saw to notice his car had been "borrowed."

Before we got to Town Hall, we stopped to pick up coffee and muffins at the *Brown Cow*. When we got there, it was still dark outside. I was not usually an early riser, so I was surprised to see a business open before the sun came up.

But Brian was already up and running when we shuffled in for our morning caffeine. He was so awake, I wondered if he had gone to bed the night before. Or ever. *Maybe Brian never slept. Maybe he was a robot!*

Woof. It was too early for me to be thinking.

I couldn't decide what to order, so Brian made me a mocha with homemade ganache, which I can say with confidence was the best drink I had ever had. I told him it was so good it made me feel like I was going blind. I was not sure if he took it as a compliment.

After the *Brown Cow*, we drove over to town hall and parked across the street, so we could intercept the mayor on her way into the office. It was Sunday, and most small-town mayors were probably sleeping in or curling up with a good book. But Mayor Delgado was famous in Pine Grove for working seven days a week, and Miss May reasoned that city hall would be the perfect place to catch Delgado off guard.

Thus commenced the sitting and waiting. In the movies, detectives get bored and fall asleep for that part. But I was so pumped to be on my first stakeout, I couldn't have slept even if Brian had mixed sleeping pills into my ganache. *OK, maybe the sleeping pills would have worked. You get my point.*

As we waited, Miss May and I tossed a few theories back and forth.

"Do you think Liz was right about the mayor and Vlad?" I asked. "Is it possible that the mayor is running for governor, and that Charles had information that would compromise her?"

Miss May shrugged. "That seems farfetched. Although it

also seems equally farfetched for two people to turn up dead in Pine Grove, so I'm not ruling anything out."

"Mayor Delgado seems ambitious to me," I said. "I bet she does want to run for governor."

"I know," Miss May said. "But if Delgado hired Vlad to kill Charles, why was Vlad still in town days after Charles turned up dead? And why did he ransack Jennifer's salon?"

I turned on my seat-warmer and tucked my legs under my butt. "That's a good point. It would be weird for a contract killer to get a room in a BnB after killing his victim. Not exactly the time to appreciate the local scenery and home-cooked food."

"That doesn't mean the mayor wasn't involved, though," Miss May said. "Why else would she have any contact with the killer?"

Goosebumps tingled up and down my arms as I gazed through the windshield. *How easy it is to forget*, I mused, *that we are hunting a murderer.*

I had a distinct case of the creeps. But Miss May was as relaxed as ever. She yawned, leaned her chair back, and told me to wake her up when the mayor arrived.

"Seriously? You're napping?"

"Just closing my eyes real quick." Miss May rolled over and let out another big yawn. I sighed. This was going to be a long morning.

For the first three hours, not much happened. I spotted Humphrey, the grumpy old regular from *Grandma's*, walking Semolina the Fat Hound. Then I spotted a few squirrels, bickering noisily as they darted across a power line.

After a while, my eyes drooped, and my mind wandered. Sleep was calling to me, and it made a pretty convincing argument. "Rest your eyes," Sleep said. "Close them for a few seconds. It'll feel sooo nice."

Just as Sleep was about to talk me into doing something I'd regret, a doe and two fawns bounded out in front of KP's car. I sat up in my seat, and my eyes sprang open. I let out a long, low, "Woooow." My breath poofed into the cold space between the seat and the windshield.

The deer and her fawns were all sinew and grace, hooved ballerinas transforming the snowy streets into their stage. I thought about waking Miss May, but the moment would seem less special to her. At the orchard, deer were so common, they were pests. But as a recovering city girl, I still thought they were beautiful pests.

I watched the deer until they disappeared behind a building. A few moments later a nice, new sedan pulled up and parked in front of city hall.

I tapped Miss May as the sedan idled. "Hey! Wake up!"

Miss May rubbed her eyes. "She's here?"

"Yes! Look!"

Miss May peered out the window as the mayor climbed out of her car and grabbed a briefcase out of the backseat.

"What do we do!?" I asked.

"We go!" Miss May unbuckled her seatbelt, jumped out of the car and hurried toward town hall. My aunt moved fast for a woman who had just been in a deep slumber. I grabbed the keys out of the ignition and followed her.

The mayor was about to enter the building when Miss May called out, "Mayor Delgado! Hi!"

Mayor Delgado turned back as Miss May and I approached. The mayor looked weary, like she thought it was way too early on a Sunday to deal with Miss May. I could relate.

"May. How are you?" The mayor smiled, ever the politician. "What are you doing here so early on a Sunday?"

"Coming to see you. What else?" Miss May smiled right

back. Both women were acting cordial, but animosity simmered beneath their polite exteriors.

"Is there a town matter you'd like to discuss? I know you don't like my streetlight initiative, but that's on the back burner right now anyway." Mayor Delgado opened the door and took a step inside. "You can bring it up at the next town meeting."

"This isn't about the streetlights," Miss May said.

Delgado turned back. "For all other town business, you'll need to schedule an appointment through my office. I wish I could see you today, but I'm swamped, as usual." The mayor tried a casual laugh, but it sounded forced and robotic.

"It's Sunday," Miss May said. "How swamped could you be?"

"The town doesn't run itself, May. I'm very swamped. I'm... the swampiest." Delgado took another step inside. "Now if you'll excuse me—"

"We know about you and the dead guy, Linda." The words were out of my mouth before I even knew I was thinking them. Miss May looked at me with impressed shock.

Mayor Delgado winced. "I don't know what you mean," she said. *Oh, she knew exactly what we meant.*

Miss May handed over the photos that Liz had given us. "Do these look familiar?"

The mayor shook her head. "This again?"

"What do you mean 'this'?" Miss May said.

"And what do you mean 'again'?" I chimed in.

The mayor looked from me to Miss May and back again.

"Come on in," Delgado said. "We better talk about this inside."

25

THE DATE-GATE SCANDAL

I grimaced as soon as I stepped into the mayor's office. Her walls were covered in diplomas, and I hate-hate-hated diplomas.

As an interior designer in New York City, I had fought a constant losing battle with clients over their diplomas. Always eager to show off their accomplishments, my clients had often dedicated entire walls in their homes to their educational achievements. "I get it," I'd say. "School is hard. But diplomas are ugly." Sometimes clients would let me take down one or two of their lesser accomplishments. But I had never convinced a single person to hide all of their degrees in a deep, dark drawer where those hideous things belonged.

Mayor Delgado was the worst diploma offender I had ever seen. *By about ten diplomas! How had she had enough time to attend this much school?* I tried not to say anything, but my inner design-snob triumphed over my politeness.

"You have a lot of diplomas," I said.

Mayor Delgado took a seat behind her desk. "Thank

you. BA, BS, JD, MFA, MBA, PhD. I worked hard for them."
Ugh. That's what they all say.

"Very impressive," Miss May said. "So. What's up with the photos of you and Vlad?"

Delgado gestured to a pair of leather chairs across from her desk. "Take a seat."

Miss May and I sat. The mayor smoothed her blazer and cleared her throat. "Can I get you water? Coffee?"

"Answers would be nice." Miss May crossed her legs and waited. Whenever my aunt got confrontational, I got nervous. Sweat sprang to my forehead and stuck my knees to the fabric of my jeans. *Sweaty kneecaps. Gross.*

"OK," Delgado said. "Fine."

The mayor took a sip of her coffee and continued, "I don't know anything about those photos. That man asked me what time it was, so I told him the time."

Miss May scoffed. "And you both happened to be under the bridge by the train tracks when this occurred?"

"Yes." Mayor Delgado did not break eye contact with Miss May.

"Linda, come on." Miss May sat back in her chair. "That story is fake. Besides, you wouldn't have asked us in here if it was that simple. Don't you think, Chelsea?"

I patted at my sweaty hairline. "Uh, with all due respect, Mrs. Mayor, that story does sound fake." *At least as fake as a couple of these diplomas*, I suspected.

Mayor Delgado grunted and adjusted her lumbar support. "Fine. I'll tell you why I really met him. But the information I am about to divulge must not leave this room."

"That depends," Miss May said. "Did you hire that man to kill Charles?"

"Of course not!" Mayor Delgado laughed. "I told you, I didn't have any money with Fitz, and neither did the town."

"But Vlad might have threatened you. Or your run for governor." Miss May paused to see if Delgado would object. *Nope.* "Maybe he tried to blackmail you to help pay back his debts."

"That's ridiculous," Delgado said. "That man, Vlad, as you call him, approached me last week. He was desperate for cash, and he wanted my money."

Everyone in town knew that Mayor Delgado came from a wealthy family. Vlad must have found out about her fortune and extorted her. *But with what dirt?*

"What kind of dirt did he have on you?" Miss May asked. *Good thing somebody was around to say what I was thinking.*

Delgado shifted in her chair. "Vlad had uh... pictures of his own."

Miss May looked at me. I shrugged. *Don't ask me.* So Miss May turned back to Delgado. "What kind of pictures?"

"They're private."

"You have to show me," Miss May said. "If you want me to clear your name."

"Clear my name of what?"

"Double homicide."

Mayor Delgado's face tightened. "I haven't been accused of any homicide. At least not that I know of."

"Look, I don't know anything official," Miss May said, "but I have it on good information that an article will soon be published, in the New York Times, perhaps, which will allege that you hired Vlad to kill Charles, after Charles got in the way of your gubernatorial bid."

The mayor shook her head. "Liz tell you that?"

"I can't say."

Delgado sighed. "That girl is killing me."

"...but is she right about any of it?" I asked.

"No!" Delgado slid open a drawer and pulled out a folder. "Liz is way off, as usual. Here." Delgado pushed the folder toward us but kept her hand on it. "Before you see these, I need your word. This must stay private."

"Of course." Miss May reached out and Delgado released the folder.

Miss May flipped open the manila cover to reveal a shocking image. "Whoa!" I said before I could stop myself. The picture showed the mayor, in a skintight dress, grinding on a tall, red-haired stranger.

Miss May shuffled to the next photo, which was racier than the first. Liz's pictures had been surprising, but these puppies were downright scandalous. Miss May was tongue-tied. "Wow. That's... You're..."

My aunt wasn't prudish or puritanical, but she was still a middle-aged woman living in a small town. And by Pine Grove standards, these snapshots were basically porn.

"Uh, so what are these pictures?" I normally wouldn't be so blunt, but my curiosity was raging harder than a metal head in a mosh pit.

"First, I'll tell you what 'Vlad' thought they were."

Miss May unglued her eyes from the pictures and look up at the mayor. "Go on."

"The day those photos were shot, I had taken a limo into Manhattan. I had gotten a room at a high-end hotel. And I had met that man, the red-haired man, in the hotel bar. That man convinced me to go dancing with him. Then we went back to the hotel together, where we did more than dance."

Whew! Let's keep this cozy, Mrs. Mayor!

She continued. "Vlad thought he had caught me

cheating on my husband. But the man in those photos is my husband."

Miss May shook her head. "Your husband is bald." *And this guy was a carrot top.*

Delgado exhaled. "That's the embarrassing part. Every couple months, my husband and I go somewhere nice and pretend to meet for the first time. You'll notice, I have a shoulder tattoo in that photo. The tattoo was also fake."

I started to laugh but stopped myself halfway, which produced a weird snort. The snort got stuck in my nose, which made me sneeze. *A familiar cycle.* It was all so silly that I ended up laughing. The mayor stared me down until I stopped laughing. "Sorry," I said. "Allergies."

Miss May swooped in to alleviate the awkwardness. "I think that's nice."

"It's unusual, I know, but it keeps things spicy." Mayor Delgado spoke with such measured diplomacy about her 'spicy' relationship, I had to swallow another snort-laugh.

Delgado reached across the desk for the folder. "May I have the photos back? It's all innocent enough, but not the kind of pictures you want leaked before you run for governor."

"So you are running." Miss May smiled.

"It's not official, but maybe in a few years. The photos?"

"Of course." Miss May closed the folder and handed it back to Delgado.

Delgado tucked the folder back into her desk and locked the drawer. "So now you know my secret."

"So it would seem," Miss May said. "And that certainly clears you in Charles' murder. But... what about Vlad? I'd be furious if someone tried to ruin my life like that. Even if he didn't get away with it."

"I was furious!" Delgado chuckled. "Are you kidding? I called the police right away."

"So what happened?" I asked.

"Vlad showed up dead the next morning." Delgado shrugged. "Of course, part of me said, 'Good riddance.' But then, part of me was sad. He was a crook, this Vlad, but he didn't deserve murder in the first."

The mayor looked down and a pall descended on the room. I wondered if Delgado's show of sympathy and solemnity was more politicking, but I decided to give her the benefit of the doubt. Murder is sad, even if you're running for governor.

After a few seconds, Miss May stood. "We should be going. Thank you for your time, Mrs. Mayor."

"You're welcome." Delgado rose and shook Miss May's hand. "I know I said to keep this between us, but perhaps you could... pass it on to Liz? Keep her from running a bogus story?"

"She's tough to wrangle, but we'll do our best. I think it'll be fine. You stay safe, OK?"

Delgado nodded. "You too."

26

ALPACAS AND EMAILS

*W*hen we walked up to *Grandma's*, a line stretched all the way down Main Street. There were at least two hundred people braving the cold for a taste of Teeny's hashbrown lasagna.

"Looks like Teeny's got a sensation on her hands," Miss May said.

I laughed. "For real. I can't remember the last time any business in Pine Grove got this kind of attention."

Miss May stiffened. "Prime apple-picking season, the orchard gets lines for hours."

I grinned at my aunt. Miss May was the most supportive, and the most competitive, person I knew. She was a sturdy woman, but her ego bruised like an overripe Granny Smith. I amended my statement, "Any business except the farm, of course."

Miss May hurried her stride as we got closer to *Grandma's*. "Is that a news van?"

Sure enough, News Channel 12 was parked outside *Grandma's*, and a slick, gray-haired anchor was standing out front with a microphone, interviewing Teeny.

"And how did you get the idea for hashbrown lasagna?" the anchorman asked. "Because the people are loving it!"

The anchor gestured to the crowd, and a group of teenagers cheered and hooted, jumping on each other's backs for a chance to be on TV.

"To be honest, Bart, the idea for this creation came to me on the toilet," Teeny said. "That's where I get a lot of my good ideas."

"You heard it here first, people! Pine Grove's very own celebrity chef brainstorms on the toilet. I love it! And this is Bartholomew Baggins, saying good eats make a good day! Signing off!"

Bart shook Teeny's hand, climbed into the news van, and just like that... he was off.

Miss May rushed over to Teeny as soon as the van pulled out. "Teeny! You were on the news!"

Teeny tittered and hugged Miss May. "I should not have said that toilet thing."

"Are you kidding?" I said. "That was the best part." I hugged Teeny too, and she squeezed me so hard I swore I heard a rib crack.

"How did all this happen?" Miss May asked.

"Petey's Internet virus post infected more people." Teeny called up toward the roof of the restaurant. "Thanks, Petey! Just think of all you would accomplish with a high school degree!"

I followed Teeny's gaze up to the roof, where Petey was on his hands and knees, scraping ice and fixing a broken shingle. He gave a sad little thumbs-up, then got back to work.

Teeny turned back. "So. What are you two doing here?"

"Uh, well... we wanted to update you on the case."

Teeny smacked her forehead. "The case! I forgot all about the case!"

"You three talking about the murders?"

I looked over, and there was one of *Grandma's* regulars, Humphrey, waiting with his fat old Bassett hound Semolina.

"Shush up, Humphrey. Go back to your place in line!" Teeny had no problem scolding her customers, especially Humphrey.

But Humphrey didn't budge. "I heard Gigley did it. Did you three see those emails he sent?"

Miss May and I exchanged a look. *How did Humphrey know about the emails?*

Humphrey pulled out a surprisingly new smartphone and began reading. "This one says 'I will kill you, Charles! I demand my money.' Then there's another that says, 'I wish death upon you.' And another that just says 'Hey Charles, wondering what is your height and weight? I need to know so I can measure a fatal dose of cyanide without wasting any cyanide.'"

Miss May hung her head. "Tom, Tom, Tom."

Humphrey nodded. "That's what I thought. It's too bad Tom's a murderer. But damn those emails cracked me up!"

"How did you get a hold of those?" Miss May asked.

"Everyone in town got them! Forwarded from Charles' account. Spooky, right? He's back from the dead."

"What is wrong with you?" Teeny asked.

Humphrey shrugged. "I don't know. In general, I don't have a lot to look forward to, but this stuff cheered me up."

Teeny dragged Humphrey to the back of the line. "OK, Humphrey. That's enough. And I told you no dogs in the restaurant!"

Humphrey yanked his arm away. "Semolina is an emotional support animal!"

"So go cry at the dog park with her!" Teeny trudged back over to me and Miss May, shaking her head. "That man makes me nuts!"

"You want to know who makes me nuts?" Miss May asked.

"Gigley," I said.

Miss May nodded. "Come on. We've got to go talk to him."

Teeny pouted. "Aw, now!? I've got a line out the door!"

"We'll fill you in later." Miss May walked out toward Main Street.

Teeny sighed. "Fine. Watch your fingers and toes, OK?"

What's that supposed to mean? Were our fingers and toes in particular danger? I instinctively curled my hands into little balls to protect my digits.

Miss May answered my question before I asked it. "Yeah, yeah. We'll be careful." *So "fingers and toes" was just a Teeny-ism.* Miss May continued, "But only if you spend some of your brilliant toilet time thinking about how to solve this case. We need it."

"Deal." Teeny and Miss May shook hands.

We left to go find Gigley, the author of the most incriminating emails ever sent.

I wondered as we headed back to the van...*Were we going to visit a killer?*

As soon as we got away from the crowd, Miss May answered the question I had been mulling over.

"There's no way Tom Gigley killed those men."

I had grown to like Gigley since I'd moved back home, so I appreciated Miss May's confidence. Still, I hadn't written him off as a suspect. Those emails were angry and mean. The exact kind of emails someone would send if they planned to murder their accountant.

"How are you so sure?" I asked.

"Because I know him. And I won't suspect him like I suspected Florence, that poor woman."

"Why are we walking toward Gigley's office then?" I asked.

Miss May picked up the pace as the old colonial that housed Gigley's office came into view down the street. "Because he's done enough to incriminate himself. Now he's being tried in the court of public opinion, and he's going to need our help."

Thirty seconds later, Miss May and I entered Gigley's office without a knock.

Gigley's secretary, Deb, was at her desk. Deb was a polite old woman with a big head of permed gray hair, and the thickest bifocals I had ever seen. She stood when we entered.

"May! What are you doing, barging in here without so much as a knock?" Deb's voice was high-pitched and frail. *Classic old biddy voice.*

"Hi, Deb. How was your cruise?" Miss May could be polite even in the face of direct confrontation.

"Oh, it was wonderful. We started off in the Czech Republic, then—"

"Sounds great. We should catch up over lunch. Is Tom in the office?" *But she could also be terse.*

Deb looked put off by Miss May's interruption. "Lunch could be fine, although I have pictures now that I'd love to show you. Germany was nice but too many sausages."

"You know, Deb. I want to give those photos my full

attention, but right now I'm in a rush. Did you say Tom was in his office?"

"OK. Lunch. Does next Tuesday work?"

"Tuesday's fine, Deb!" Miss May raised her voice but reeled it in before she continued. "Tuesday is great. My treat. I'll even buy dessert if you tell me if Tom is in."

"I can't have dessert. Doctor says I need to cut back on sugar, flour, marshmallows, anything white."

"Deb!"

"Oh, right. Mr. Gigley. He hasn't come in yet today. I'm sure he'll be here soon."

Miss May sighed. "He didn't call?"

"Nope. He does this sometimes. Sleeps in. Runs errands. He's the boss, so what do I care?"

Thud! Thud! Thud! Someone pounded on the door and a voice boomed from outside. "Police! Open up!"

Deb's face reddened. "Police? What could they want?"

Miss May shrugged. "Do you want me to open it?"

Deb climbed to her feet in a daze, stumbled toward the door and cracked it. There stood Wayne in all his hunky glory. Windswept hair. Cheeks rosy from the cold. Every inch of his broad six-foot frame poised for action.

"Hi, I'm Detective Wayne Hudson. This is my partner Sunshine Flanagan. We're here to speak with Mr. Gigley. Can you get him out here right away?"

"Sunshine?" I couldn't hide the amused incredulity in my voice.

Flanagan placed her hand on her holster. "Do you have a problem with that name, ma'am?"

Wayne turned to Flanagan. "Stay cool, Flanagan."

Flanagan kept her hand on her holster and took a step toward me. "My mother loved the name. Thought it was nice and warm. Thought it would make me a happy kid."

"...you seem happy," I said.

"I am happy!" Flanagan shouted and stepped toward me, but Wayne blocked her path.

"Whoa, whoa," Wayne said. "Everybody calm down. Nobody's questioning your happiness. Or your name. Right, Chelsea? You like the name?"

"Sunshine is a wonderful name," I agreed, raising my hands in a gesture of surrender. "I'm so, so sorry."

Wayne narrowed his eyes. "Hold up. What are you two doing here, anyway?"

"We came to see Mr. Gigley about an alpaca we want to buy," I lied. *Classic Chelsea excuse. Completely unbelievable.* But, as always, I stuck with it."The alpaca is adorable. She would get along great with our tiny horse, See-Saw. We needed Mr. Gigley to draw up the paperwork for the sale."

Wayne furrowed his brow. "You were going to use a lawyer to draft a legally binding contract for an alpaca sale?"

Miss May stepped forward. "Alpaca law is arcane and convoluted. We needed a legal eagle to make sure we weren't getting screwed. I'd do it myself, but alpacas were never my specialty. More of a llama woman." *How was Miss May keeping a straight face right now?* "But, alas, Gigley's not here. So now we'll head home to bake cookies and make jam. You know, orchard stuff."

Wayne and Flanagan exchanged a confused look. "OK, I guess," Wayne said. "Good to see you Chelsea."

"You too," I said. Then I added, just for good measure. "Nice to officially meet you, Sunshine."

Flanagan replied with an angry glare, then Miss May hugged Deb goodbye, and we left.

Deb called after us, "See you Tuesday, May!"

27

CURVY AND CARSICK

*W*hen we left Gigley's office, I saw Wayne's cruiser parked outside, and my stomach did a backflip. Inside the office, Wayne's presence had felt familiar and non-threatening. Part of me had welcomed his arrival, *let's be honest.*

But seeing Wayne's cop car, I remembered how serious the stakes of our investigation were. If we caught whoever had killed Charles and Vlad, then a person would go to jail. Maybe for life. And if we didn't catch them...I didn't want to imagine that.

We needed to solve this mystery, before the killer struck again. Or worse, before the police pinned the murder on the wrong person.

Miss May must have felt a similar sense of urgency, because as soon as we exited the office, she power-walked back down Main Street toward where we had parked.

I hurried after her, but I had to take two steps for every one of Miss May's long strides, so it was hard to keep up.

"Miss May," I said. "Wait up!"

"No time to wait," Miss May said. "This thing is life or death."

Miss May placed a call and listened as it rang.

I jogged until I was side by side with Miss May. "Who are you calling? Gigley?"

Miss May hung up. "Yup. No answer."

"Where do you think he is?"

"I know without a doubt where that man is." Miss May stopped walking and turned to me.

"He's in Connecticut."

"So we're going to Connecticut?"

Miss May grinned. "Yup. And I'm warning you now, it's curvy roads the whole way there, and I don't want to hear a peep out of you."

"I can't help it. I get carsick!"

"Then stay home. Or get your darn license!"

Miss May unlocked the van and climbed in. "Are you coming or not?"

She started the car, and I felt a preliminary bout of nausea.

Connecticut.

Uch.

I kept my mouth shut for the first hundred and fifty curves on the curvy, curvy road out to Connecticut. But once Miss May veered around number one-fifty-one, my lid popped off.

"You're driving worse than Teeny!"

"How dare you," Miss May gasped. "It's not me. It's the roads."

I belched and clutched my stomach.

Miss May rolled the window down. "If you're going to spew, do it out the window."

I stuck my head outside, but my nose froze in the blistering wind. "Too cold, too cold! Window up!"

Miss May hesitated. "No puking?"

"No puking. I promise."

Miss May raised the window. She slowed to take a hairpin turn. "That better?"

"Not really." I belched again. "Why did we have to trek all the way out to Connecticut anyway? What could Gigley be doing out here?"

"Gigley grew up in Connecticut, in a beautiful old Victorian. His parents left him the house. Gigley still comes out here when he needs to clear his head."

"How do you know all that?" I asked.

"Tom and I have been friends for thirty years," Miss May said. "I'm worried about that man. Sending all those ridiculous messages. It's not the Gigley I know."

"He must be stressed about his missing money."

Miss May took another curve. I burped again, and this time a hiccup came out at the same time. It sounded like a gross frog dry-heaving.

Miss May chuckled. "Close your eyes. That always helped when you were a kid."

"But that's not a good copilot move. I'm supposed to keep you company."

Miss May shook her head. "You're just burping, Chels. Relax."

When I opened my eyes, Miss May was shifting the van

into park in front of a gorgeous winter meadow. The ground was such a pure, bright white, it hurt my eyes.

A thick layer of snow undulated across a beautiful field. A frozen pond glimmered like a mirror in the sun. And a blue jay fluttered between the branches of a massive evergreen.

I rubbed my eyes and blinked. "Whoa."

"Yeah," Miss May said. "I thought you might say that."

I sat up to get a better look out the window, and I noticed parallel tire tracks indenting a long driveway.

At the top of the driveway sat a massive pink Victorian house, three stories high, with several turrets, light yellow lacing, and a large wraparound porch. The bright pink mansion seemed like a wad of bubblegum flung against the pure snow.

I had always dreamed of decorating a home with such massive character and charm. I couldn't wait to see inside.

"That is where Gigley grew up?" I asked.

Miss May smirked. "It is."

I laughed. "Weird."

"What's so funny? You didn't peg him as a pink house man?"

"I did not."

Our chuckle lasted a few more seconds, then Miss May chunked the van back into gear. I reached out to stop her. "Could we walk? It's so peaceful."

Miss May pulled up on the curb and parked. "Alright," she said. "Let's go."

A thin layer of ice topped the fresh powder, so our feet crunched as we trudged up the driveway. I fantasized about living in Connecticut as we walked. *I could be a Connecticut person, right? I could make quiche.*

As we got closer to the home, I admired its complicated,

asymmetrical shape, and its delicate, decorative trim. I considered the pre-fab homes of modern America and shook my head. Back when Gigley's house had been built, I assumed sometime in the late 1800s, people had appreciated craftsmanship. That craftsmanship was still evident two hundred years later, in all its perfect pink glory.

As we got closer, my admiration shifted to intimidation. This house was huge, and the charm I had noticed from the street was imposing at close range. As we climbed the creaky steps up to the front porch, the whole place seemed... haunted.

I stopped walking halfway up the stairs. "Did Gigley's parents...die here?"

Miss May turned back. "Chels. No!" Ding-dong! Miss May rang the doorbell. "But someone did."

I hurried up the steps in a panic. "Wait, what? Who?"

Miss May shrugged. "I don't know. Previous owner, I think. An elderly woman."

"Are you serious!? What happened?"

"Nobody could figure it out. Some people said she was murdered, but there was never any evidence. Probably she was just old."

I put my hands on my hips. "Oh, well that's comforting."

Miss May cupped her hands and peered in a side window. "It's not like the place is haunted. Gigley lived here his whole life." She turned back. "Follow me."

Miss May thumped down the porch, then walked around the side of the house. I followed her through a rickety gate into the backyard.

Behind the house was an open field with three enormous weeping willows. I had barely taken in the creepy-but-breathtaking sight when a sudden wind stirred the dormant snow, and a thick white mist swirled around me.

When the mini-blizzard settled, I looked up and noticed an enormous statue of a man, at least fifteen feet high. The figure towered over us, scowling and severe.

"OK," Miss May said. "Maybe it's haunted."

I wiped snowflakes from my eyelashes. "What's with that statue?"

"I have no idea," Miss May said. "Let's find out."

Miss May marched to the foot of the statue. "There's an inscription! 'Here stands a monument to courage and compassion. The most noble of all human qualities.' Well! That doesn't sound spooky!" She squinted at the statue. "Hold up, there's a second part."

"Miss May! I want to go!"

"'May evil keep its distance. For the Devil hath visited this home enough.'"

My complexion paled. "You're making that up!"

Miss May shook her head. "I'm not that creative."

Another gale swept through the yard. A willow bough swayed and snapped. Miss May zipped her coat to her neck and yelled over the deep howl.

"What?" I shouted.

Miss May yelled again, but her voice disappeared into the snowy torrent. We stood looking at each other, waiting out the wind. When the sound abated, another voice yelled from house.

"What are you two doing here!?"

I shrieked and stumbled backwards. A powdery drift broke my fall and I landed with a phwumph. When I glanced up, there was Gigley, standing at the back door.

He did not look happy.

28

MADMEN AND MANSIONS

*G*igley held the door open, and Miss May and I walked into the house. I had hoped Gigley's place would be warm and welcoming, but I got a chill when I stepped inside.

We entered into what looked like it used to be a drawing room. Painter's cloth covered hulking furniture. Dusty books lined the shelves. And an enormous oil painting of an 18th century couple hung askew above the couch. Neither the man nor the woman in the portrait looked happy. *Frankly*, I mused, *they look like the Devil hath visited them enough.*

Over by the far wall, someone had pried up several floorboards. Next to the ripped-up planks was a huge stack of books, each of which had pages torn from the middle. The place seemed like a madman had ransacked it.

I looked at Gigley.

T-shirt. Sweatpants. Face smeared with dirt and soot. I had never seen Pine Grove's most eminent lawyer in anything but a suit, and I wondered... *Was Gigley the madman?*

Miss May got straight to the point. "What the heck is going on in here, Gigley?"

"What the heck to you!" Gigley shoved his hands in his pockets. "Who do you think you are, barging in here like this?"

"You told us to come in!"

"That was after you barged into my yard," said Gigley.

Miss May softened her tone. "We're here to help. You hired us, remember?"

Gigley grunted. "You want to help, find out who forwarded those emails from Charles' account."

"Forget about Charles for a second, Tom. What's the matter with you?"

Gigley sighed, and his shoulders slouched. He was an articulate man, and I'd never seen him at a loss for words.

Miss May sat on the edge of the couch. Dust plumed around her. "You're being crazy, Tom. First with the emails, now with disappearing to Connecticut. I'm worried about you."

"You're not here to question me because you think I'm guilty like everyone else in town?"

"Of course not," Miss May said. "We already knew about the emails, remember? Everyone else finding out didn't change anything."

Gigley cleared his throat. "I'll admit that I have developed a bad habit with angry emails."

Miss May laughed. "That goes without being said."

"I've been frustrated. That's all," Gigley said. "When I was a young man, people were good to each other. You had to be. No one moved away, or 'started over.' They lived around the same people their entire lives, and their reputations meant something. Now everything is so...impersonal. I wanted someone to be accountable for their actions. Pathetic, I know."

"It's not pathetic," Miss May said. "Those emails are hysterical. And well-written. You should publish them in a book."

Gigley laughed and shook his head. "They're pathetic, May."

"Either way, it doesn't matter," Miss May stood. "So you sent some emails. It's not a smoking gun."

"It is in this day and age," Gigley said.

Miss May sighed and ran her fingers along the dusty bookshelf. She stopped when she arrived at the pried-up floor boards near Gigley. "What's going on here, by the way?"

"Exactly what it looks like," Gigley said. "I'm looking for my hidden cash."

Miss May narrowed her eyes. "I'm going to ignore the fact that you have 'hidden cash,' and instead ask a more pressing question. What do you need it for?"

"I need the money to start over somewhere new. I haven't been charged with anything, so I should be free to go wherever I want."

Miss May cast a glance my way. I wondered if she was thinking what I was thinking: *That sounds like what a guilty man would say.*

"What?" Gigley asked.

Miss May turned to him. "You must realize how guilty this makes you look, Tom." *Yup, same brain wave.* "Digging up money so you can disappear."

"So you do think I did it!"

"I didn't say that. But...you could tell me. If you did. I would understand."

My shoulders scrunched up toward my ears, a sure sign

that my conflict radar was going off. Miss May hadn't come here thinking Gigley was guilty, but she was probing for a confession. If the tension didn't break soon, my neck was going to disappear into my collarbones.

Could Gigley be the murderer?

"This is unconscionable, May! You're accusing me. Like everyone else."

"I am not. I'm saying that...you look guilty."

"How is that different from leveling an accusation?"

I took a tiny step forward, trying to de-hunch my shoulders. "It seems different to me."

"Well, it's not!" Gigley slammed his fist down on the bookshelf, and I took a big step back.

Gigley held up his hands. "I'm sorry. That was...uncalled for. I should not have yelled. Especially not at you, Chelsea. You're an innocent bystander."

Miss May stood her ground. "I don't think you're a murderer, Tom. But I do think you're acting mighty suspicious."

Gigley crossed to an armchair, pulled the paint cloth off and plopped down. More dust plumed around him. He coughed. "If you must know, I have an alibi for the night Charles was killed."

Miss May waved away invisible dust. "I'd like to know what it is."

Gigley sighed. "The police said Charles was killed the night before you found him, right, Chelsea?"

I nodded.

Gigley reached into his pocket with an old-man groan and pulled out his cell. "I spent the entirety of that night sending angry emails. Not to Charles. There were... others."

Gigley opened his email app, poked around, and handed me the phone.

I peeked at the phone and tried to swallow my shock. But a squeal slipped out of my lips before I could zip them.

There were hundreds of emails, sent with under a minute between them, each with an angry subject line, like "HOW DARE YOU!?" or "EVERYONE YOU LOVE SHOULD DIE."

I peeled my eyes from the phone and stared at Gigley. "Did you send all these emails to the cable company?"

Gigley winced. "Four hundred and forty-one emails to Carter Cable, all sent between eight PM and two AM. I took a break for a slice of cake at around ten, but that only lasted five minutes."

There was a long, pronounced silence. Then Miss May laughed. "Tom Gigley, you are out of your mind!"

"I told you I'm not proud of the emails. But Carter's got a monopoly in Pine Grove, and it's not fair!"

"It's true," I said. "Carter is the only option in the city too. And their customer service is abysmal."

"Do not get me started on that customer service!" Gigley said. "More like customer...annoyance."

"What did they do to you?" I asked. "Specifically."

Gigley threw his hands up in the air, outraged. "They wanted to charge me extra to watch baseball. Isn't that ridiculous? Baseball has always come free with basic cable, and that's how it's supposed to be. Obviously, I should have handled things in a more professional manner. But the sentiment was spot on."

Miss May reached out and took the phone. "Let me see those emails, Chelsea."

"You don't need to read them," Gigley said. "It's embarrassing."

"One email, then I'll stop." Miss May scrolled through the phone with a smile. "Oh boy! These subject lines are killing me. Here's one: 'CARTER COMMUNICATIONS: BURN IN A FIERY INFERNO.' Little redundant, isn't it?"

Gigley hung his head. "That one is bad."

Miss May cleared her throat and read the email. "Dear Carter Communications: You are despicable. Your CEO looks like a toad, and he is ruining the great game of baseball. I demand free baseball with my basic package. If you do not meet this request, I will have no choice but to burn down the homes of all your employees, post haste. Regards, Tom Gigley ESQ." Miss May shook her head. "Tom!"

"I know!" Gigley reddened. "The messages do not reflect well on my character."

"There's an understatement," Miss May said. "Did you get your baseball?"

"No," Gigley said. "They took away my cable, then they threatened to sue. Now I have to go to the electronics store any time I want to watch a game."

Miss May and I cracked up laughing. The image of Tom Gigley, in his fresh-pressed, tailored suits, watching baseball in Pine Grove's dingy electronics store was too much to handle.

"You do not watch the games in the store," Miss May said, once she caught her breath.

Gigley crossed his arms. "Yes, I do. And the employees like it. They watch with me sometimes."

Miss May and I burst into a new fit of giggles. Gigley waved us off.

"Laugh it up, you two. The point is, I have an alibi."

"You have over four hundred alibis," I said.

At that, Miss May laughed so hard I thought she might pass out. "Four hundred alibis!

Gigley squirmed in his chair. "Stop laughing, May! Those terrible emails are the only thing standing between me and incarceration. They might very well be the best thing that has ever happened to me."

"So why dig up your money and run?" Miss May asked.

"I told you! They're embarrassing. Everybody already knows about my ridiculous emails to Charles. I can't have them find out about this cable company nightmare, too. I'll lose clients. My reputation will be irrevocably soiled."

"Alright," Miss May said. "Don't run yet. Let us catch the real killer. Then you can burn the emails in a 'fiery inferno,' and we can all pretend it never happened."

"Deal," Gigley stood. "Now let's get out of here. This place is haunted."

29

HIDE NOR HAIRDRESSER

$\mathcal{T}$he next day, I woke bright and semi-early to the sounds of Miss May baking. Miss May often baked to declutter her thoughts when she had a big problem to solve. I hoped that in the wee hours of that particular morning, she had come up with a new theory about the murders in Pine Grove. I also hoped there might be some fresh Appie Oaters for breakfast.

When I stumbled into the kitchen, my nose confirmed my hopes, at least about the Appie Oaters. Miss May had a dozen mixing bowls lined up beside jars of preserves and nutmeg and cinnamon. A dusting of flour coated her entire body. She'd been at this for a while.

"Morning," she said when she saw me. "You're just in time to help. Measure six cups of flour into that bowl?"

I grabbed the flour and took my time measuring it out.

"We got a rush order this morning," Miss May said. "Five hundred pumpkin, five hundred chocolate chip. By tomorrow."

"Oh," I said. "I figured you were stress-baking. Contemplating the investigation."

"Oh no, I am stress-baking," Miss May said. "I've already made enough dough for two thousand pumpkin, two thousand chocolate chip. And fifteen batches of Appie Oaters."

I laughed. "And? Has it worked? Have you had any breakthroughs?"

Miss May thudded dough onto the counter and punched it.

"I'll take that as a no."

Miss May glanced up at me. "You're so perceptive."

"I try," I said, attempting to lighten the mood. I continued with a gentler approach. "Would you like to, perhaps, talk about the case? It might help to bat some theories around."

"I thought you'd never ask." Miss May tasted a little fleck of dough. "Vanilla?"

I handed the vanilla over, and Miss May added a dash to her dough.

"So," she said. "The way I see it, we have two dead bodies and no good suspects."

"That's not true," I said. "All this investigating we've done...we have to have a good suspect."

"Who?" Miss May asked. "It wasn't Gigley. He was too busy sending rage-mail to kill Charles, and he had no motive to kill the bookie. And it wasn't Florence. She's deep in the throes of mourning, and everyone knows it. Who does that leave?"

I picked a chocolate chip out of the dough and ate it. "Uh...I have no idea."

I reached out to grab another chocolate chip, but Miss May smacked my hand away. "No dough until we figure this out! Or at least until we figure out what we should do next."

I pouted. Miss May pulled the dough further away and shielded it from me.

"What about the mayor?" I asked.

Miss May balled up the dough and laid the cookies out on a baking sheet. "Vlad tried to extort her, so she called the cops. What about her?"

"I don't know. Vlad did show up dead the next day. And he did have information the mayor wanted to hide."

"So she killed the guy, risking her life and her freedom, to keep the public from seeing photos of her dancing with her husband-in-a-wig? She's too smart for that."

Miss May slid the tray of cookies into the oven. "Besides, Delgado said she didn't have any money with Charles. And I've got to believe that the same person killed both these men."

"Then all we have to do is figure out who had the motive to kill both Charles and the bookie," I said.

Miss May gasped and turned back from the oven. "Jennifer."

I scrunched up my face. "You think? I mean, she's catty. But double homicide catty?"

"You said it yourself," Miss May said. "We need to find someone who had a motive to kill both men. Jennifer was having relations with Charles, right?"

"Yeah..."

"And the whole reason we tried to find the bookie is because she described him to us as the guy who ransacked her house."

"That's true," I said. "Maybe he came after her again, so she killed him in self-defense."

"Or maybe he knew something," Miss May said. "And she wanted him dead."

Miss May was on her phone before we even got out to the van.

"Who are you calling?" I asked.

"Trying Jennifer at the salon, but it keeps ringing. No answer." Miss May hung up.

"Is that unusual?"

"I'd say so. That girl picks up the phone at least twice every time she cuts my hair."

"Sounds like her," I said as I climbed into the passenger seat of the bus. "Does Jennifer have a haunted house in Connecticut we can visit?"

Miss May shook her head, ignoring my effort at levity. "I don't think so."

"So what do we do now?"

Miss May flomped behind the steering wheel. "Drive around and try to find her."

I scoffed. "That's it? That's the plan? Not a very scientific process."

"It's a small town," Miss May said. "If she's in Pine Grove, we'll spot her."

"Unless she took off for good," I said.

"Right," Miss May shifted into drive and headed off the farm. "Unless she took off for good. With all our money."

Before we drove into town, Miss May decided to swing by Jennifer's salon 'just for good measure.' We pulled up to an apocalyptic scene.

A line of shaggy-haired customers milled about like zombies on Jennifer's driveway, tapping on the windows, or pacing back and forth, confused. Jennifer was no longer overseeing her business, or at the very least, she hadn't been there all morning.

Although I had suspected Jennifer wouldn't be at work, my skin still clammed up like a moist towelette when I saw all those baffled costumers. It was not like Jennifer to leave money on the table. *Unless she took off with Charles' stolen fortune,* I thought. Better that than stick around and go to jail.

After we checked Jennifer's, Miss May and I headed to *Grandma's* to pick up Teeny. Teeny had been downright furious that she'd missed catching the last bad guy, so Miss May planned to invite Teeny along on the hunt for the missing Jennifer.

When we got to the restaurant, there was such a mob in the vestibule that we had to elbow our way through the front door. And when we finally got inside, we couldn't find Teeny anywhere...Until she ran past us so fast it blew up my skirt like an NYC subway breeze.

"Teeny!" Miss May called out.

"No time, May!" Teeny crossed the restaurant, grabbed a mop and wiped up a spill under a vacant table.

"You're going to want to make time for this, Teeny," Miss May said.

Teeny turned to us with her blue eyes in a manic panic. "I can't make time, May! Do you see this? Do you see what that hashbrown lasagna has done to me? I just want things to go back to normal. Why won't they go back to normal!?"

"OK, T. Calm down." Miss May took Teeny by the shoulders. "Your restaurant is successful. This is a good thing. Don't worry about me and Chelsea. Just keep calm and hashbrown on."

Miss May turned to go, but Teeny caught her arm. "Wait!"

Miss May turned back.

"You're not about to take down the bad guy...are you?" Teeny shrunk and made her most pitiable face.

Miss May hesitated. I could tell what she was thinking:

Should we tell a little white lie to protect Teeny's fragile heart? But we didn't get the chance. Miss May's momentary uncertainty was all the answer Teeny needed.

"No!" Teeny tossed her mop against the wall. "You have to wait!"

Miss May shook her head. "We can't. There's a killer on the loose."

"Darn...tootin'!" Teeny stomped and crossed her arms. "This damn restaurant is ruining all my mystery fun! You at least have to tell me who it is. Please."

Miss May looked over her shoulder to make sure no one was listening. Then she looked over her other shoulder. The coast was clear, so she leaned in and whispered the name of the suspect into Teeny's ear.

Miss May's subtle whisper was an exercise in futility. As soon as Teeny heard Jennifer's name, she smacked her knee and yelled, "That little hair-cutting brat!"

"We don't know anything for sure," Miss May said. "In fact, we don't even know where she is. That's part of why we came here."

"Has she been into the restaurant today?" I asked. "Or yesterday?"

Teeny narrowed her eyes and looked into the distance. Then, after twenty seconds, she turned back. "Nope. Haven't seen her. But I'll tell you if I do."

"Thanks," Miss May said. "And Teeny? Enjoy your success."

Teeny's shoulders relaxed a bit, but she waved Miss May off. "Yeah, yeah. This HBL will be the death of me!"

"Worse ways to go," Miss May said. "Now you better get back into that kitchen, because something's on fire."

My gaze snapped to the kitchen, where smoke blossomed from an unknown source. Teeny pushed her way through the crowd to extinguish the fire, and Miss May and I slipped out the back, laughing.

30

BEACH BUNNY

*T*he next stop on our whirling dervish tour of Pine Grove was the *Brown Cow*, our cozy little coffee spot right in the heart of town. When we entered, I was glad to see Rita working behind the coffee bar. Rita hadn't always been an ally of mine, but she'd recently become a single mother, and parenthood had shifted her attitude from too-cool-for-school to please-be-my-friend-and-give-me-free-diapers.

"Chelsea! Hey!" Rita came out from behind the counter and hugged me and Miss May as we approached. "I haven't seen you two in forever!"

"How was maternity leave?" I asked.

"Are you kidding me? More like maternity-don't-leave-your-house. I'm so happy to be back at work!" Rita sighed. "Don't get me wrong, Little Vinny's a blessing. But I can only handle so many poop-filled blessings per day!"

Rita's single mom-dom was not by choice. Her baby-daddy had been kind of a deadbeat. And he was also, well, dead. So she'd had it kind of rough.

Rita shook off her self-pity and mustered her best customer-service-smile. "What can I get you two?"

Miss May ordered a couple drinks, heavy on the cream, heavy on the sugar, light on the coffee. Once Rita started making them, Miss May leaned on the bar and adopted her most casual tone.

"Hey uh, has Jennifer Paul been in here today by any chance? I'm dying for a haircut but can't get through."

"Yeah," Rita said. "Jennifer was here like twenty minutes ago. She was acting weird, though."

I tried to imitate Miss May's casual tone, but my voice came out like a choking cat. *Maybe Wayne had been right about me having hairballs.* "Weird how?" I squeaked.

"Weird weird." Rita emphasized the second 'weird' like it would explain something. It didn't.

"Totally," I croaked. "Double weird." *What does that mean?*

Rita foamed Miss May's drink and dusted cinnamon on top. "She was wearing little jean shorts and a crop top, for one thing. Oh! And a big summer hat."

"That qualifies as weird," Miss May said. "It's ten degrees outside."

"I know," Rita said. "My fake eyelashes froze in the car over night!"

"What else was weird?" I asked, getting a handle on my strangled cat vibe.

"She was wearing a bikini under that crop top," Rita said. "I saw the polka-dots. And she kept talking about how she's a certified lifeguard. She even asked me if I had sunscreen!"

Miss May and I exchanged a worried look.

"So by weird you meant like, insane," I said.

"I try to stay away from words like that," Rita said. "But

yeah, something shattered inside her angry brain. Did you say you wanted cream in this?"

Did I want cream? Who could answer a question like that at a time like this?! Our prime suspect was losing her marbles. She could strike again at any moment!

"Chelsea?" Miss May said. "Do you want cream?"

I snapped out of it. "Cream. Yes. Lots, please. I don't want to taste the coffee at all."

"You got it," Rita handed me the drink. "Take a sip and tell me if you want it any different."

I sipped and offered a weak, "Yum."

But I didn't register the taste at all. I was too preoccupied with Jennifer and her summer adventure. In the freezing cold.

When we got to Hastings Pond, I knew Jennifer would be there. But I was still stunned to see her sunbathing on the shore like we were knee-deep in the dog days of summer.

The weirdest part was that Jennifer looked comfortable. Relaxed, even. She was wearing a cute polka-dot bikini, she had earbuds in her ears, and she thumbed through a copy of a tabloid like it was a typical Sunday Funday. An iced latte from the *Brown Cow* was wedged into the snow beside her.

Miss May and I hovered at the edge of the beach. We were only ten feet away, but Jennifer didn't notice us.

"Let's be extra gentle in this conversation," Miss May said.

I nodded. "Goes without saying."

"OK," Miss May eyed Jennifer. "She could be dangerous."

"Kid gloves on," I mimed slipping on a pair.

Miss May nodded. Then she took a deep breath and hooked her arm in mine. And we walked onto the snow-covered beach, one careful step at a time.

Jennifer didn't notice our approach, even when we were practically standing on top of her. Miss May cleared her throat. No response. Miss May tried again, enunciating a loud, "Ahem!"

Jennifer looked up with big, glazed eyes. Her hair was matted, like she hadn't washed it for days. "Miss May. Chelsea. Hi. Isn't it lovely out here today?"

"It sure is," Miss May said.

"I needed to take some 'me' time. After everything that's happened."

"That makes sense." I sat beside Jennifer. "Do you mind if I, er... catch some rays beside you?"

"Sure." Jennifer scooted over to make room on her blanket.

"The beach always clears my mind when I'm feeling down," she said. "And I've been feeling real bad since Charles died. That stupid idiot!"

Jennifer's mournful attitude was an unexpected turn of events. Up until that moment, Jennifer had denied even knowing Charles. We'd suspected she was having an affair, but she'd been closed off and adamant that she'd never spoken to the CPA. Miss May seamlessly adapted the new narrative.

Miss May zipped up her coat and tried to hide her shivers. "That's right. You and Charles were, uh—"

"We were in love! At least I loved him. And I thought he loved me too. He told me to buy whatever I wanted. To treat myself like a queen. 'Get a credit card, and I'll pay the bills,' he said. So I did! I upgraded my salon, I ordered half the furniture catalog. Every month I forwarded him the bill, and he said he paid it. He said he had all the money in Pine Grove to play with."

Miss May inhaled sharply. Charles had obviously been stealing from his clients, and that hurt. *Were we going to see that money again?* My aunt kept her cool, though. "Let me guess. He didn't pay the bills."

"Worse! He used the cards to buy himself things, too. And he used cash advances to pay off his gambling debt. Anything to avoid spending his own money."

Jennifer looked down. "That selfish. Greedy. Horrible..." She broke into a sob and pounded the snow with her fists. "He was supposed to take me to the beach. He promised he'd leave his grumpy old wife and take me anywhere I wanted to go. Now he's gone. And I'm glad! He got what he deserved."

Miss May and I exchanged a look. *That got real. Fast.*

Miss May squatted beside Jennifer. "Hey. It's OK. You're at the beach now, right?"

"It is not OK!" Jennifer stood up. "What are you doing here anyway? Is this...are you investigating me!? Get away!"

Jennifer backed toward the pond. The water was frozen on top, but it creaked under her weight.

"Jennifer..." I stood and tiptoed onto the ice. "The uh, the water's not really warm enough for swimming today. Why don't you come back to the beach?"

Jennifer's lips were blue around the edges and her skin looked paper-white. I reached out a hand.

"No!" She yelled. She took another step back. With a deafening crack, the ice gave way beneath her.

I yelped. Miss May gulped. But Jennifer barely registered the temperature as she tumbled into the water. She flailed in the freezing slush. "Get away! This is my beach! I don't want you here!"

I wanted to help, to move, to do anything, but I was more frozen than the pond. Usually, Miss May took charge in these situations, but for once she seemed paralyzed too. *This was just all so strange.*

Jennifer's splashing got louder and louder, until another noise rose in the distance...the approaching wail of sirens.

The cops were coming.

As the police arrived and surrounded Jennifer, a lump swelled in my throat. I tried to force it down, but it only seemed to get bigger. *Ugh. I bet it's the size of a softball. Bigger. Probably visible from space.*

Jennifer had killed two people. In cold blood. But she had also trusted the wrong guy, a guy she had mistakenly loved, and that circumstance was all too familiar to me.

Yeah, she was probably a murderer. But Jennifer was a victim, too. And as the cops pulled her out of the freezing pond, shivering in her tiny polka dot bikini, she looked way more like the victim than the killer.

Miss May and I watched as hot, sexy Sunshine Flanagan loaded Jennifer into the back of a squad car.

I noticed Wayne standing nearby. He caught my eye and sauntered over. "This was a tough one, huh?"

I nodded.

Wayne shook his head. "Can't believe she killed that Vlad guy with a pair of scissors."

Miss May and I gasped. *Wait. What? Jennifer stabbed Vlad with scissors?*

"Oh. You two didn't know that, I guess," Wayne said.

"Uch. So now I divulged secret information. Terrific. This is why you can't be investigating these cases!"

"It's fine, Wayne," I reassured. "You can trust us."

Miss May nodded. "Now. Tell us more about those scissors?"

Wayne blew into his hands to warm them. "There's nothing to tell. We found the scissors this afternoon under a bridge somewhere. Wrapped in a flier for Jennifer's salon. We put two and two together. Came straight out to Jennifer's place, saw the three of you across the water, enjoying this fine day at the beach."

Miss May and I looked at one another, but neither of us could form words. Murdering someone with a pair of scissors was crazy.

About as crazy as sunbathing in the middle of February.

Wayne broke the silence. "Isn't that a classic way for a barber to off someone?" Wayne said.

"Women aren't barbers," I said. "They're hairdressers."

Wayne scoffed. "Thank you, Professor Knows Everything."

"So Jennifer one hundred percent killed Vlad?" Miss May's brow knotted in concentration.

Wayne nodded. "Scissors plunged right into the back. Gruesome. But you use what you have, right?"

"Did she kill Charles with scissors too?" I asked.

Wayne looked around to check for other officers. "I should not be sharing this information. But no. The weird thing is, Charles technically froze to death. Had a weird mix of toxins in his body, including some rare floral extract that a lot of people think is hard to detect, but, well, science. But the flower juice didn't kill him. The cold did. Jennifer must've lured him into the woods and left him there."

Miss May sighed. "I guess it's solved, then."

"What's the matter?" Wayne smirked. "Disappointed we found the murder weapon before you?"

Miss May gave Wayne a tight smile. "I'm disappointed two people died and a young woman ended up in jail."

"Right," Wayne said. "Well uh, I'll see you around."

Wayne walked to his car. Just like that, Mabel and Chelsea Thomas had solved another case. With some help from the police, I guess. But only a little.

31

BAD GUYS AND GIRLS

I awoke that night with Miss May standing above me, shaking me by the shoulders. "Chelsea! Get up! Get out of bed!"

Groan. "What time is it?

"It's almost six AM. Not that early."

Double groan. "Six AM is early for everyone except farmers."

"I don't care what time it is." Miss May yanked my arm. "Jennifer's innocent."

I sat up on my elbow and rubbed my eyes. "She is?"

Miss May nodded like a crazed puppy and yanked at my arm again. I wondered if she needed to go out and pee. Then I had a darker thought.

"That means the killer is still out there," I murmured.

"Hence the arm tugging and the waking up and the let's go already."

"OK. I'm sorry. I'm processing." I sat up and took a sip of water from the cup on my nightstand. "They found the weapon. The police said she was guilty."

"Since when do the police have any idea what they're talking about?"

"Sometimes they get it right." I took another sip of water. *But sometimes they don't.*

Miss May hurried across the room and flipped on the lights. "What are you doing sipping that water? Stop being so contemplative and get up! Come on!"

I squinted against the brightness. "Hold on. How do you know she didn't do it?"

Miss May smiled, proud. "The scissors. The flower. It all makes sense."

I wiped sleep from the corners of my eyes. "Doesn't make sense to me."

"I'll show you what I mean."

Miss May tossed me my winter jacket and a bra and walked out of the room. I called after her, "Do you not think I should wear a shirt for this?"

But Miss May was already thumping down the stairs, ready to catch the bad guy.

This time for real.

"Tell me who did it!" I begged Miss May as she sped through town. "Please!"

"No way, girlie. You have all the information you need. We both did, all along. You can figure this out."

"It was the mayor!

Miss May shook her head.

"It was Flanagan! It was one of the bookie's cronies from the city! It was Buzz Aldrin!"

"Hey. Don't you besmirch Buzz Aldrin in this car, young lady."

"You won't tell me anything."

Miss May took a wild turn, tires screeching. "That's right. I won't. I'm either going to get there, and you'll see for yourself, or you'll figure it out on your own."

"That's not safe," I said. "You should tell me who we're going to catch. Is this someone I might want to use my karate on? If so, I should limber up. Get my donkey kick ready."

Miss May chuckled. "I do not suspect your donkey kick will be necessary. Anyway, you've got that power on standby, limber or not."

May drove sixty miles per hour past the sleeping businesses on Main Street. I held on for dear life. "Whoa! Speed racer over here!"

"You bet!"

We hurtled toward one of the mayor's new traffic lights in the center of town. Miss May smirked. "Watch this."

Vroom! She blasted through the light and hung a sharp right turn out of town.

"Miss May! There are cameras on those lights."

"That's why I did it."

I laughed.

"Also, I figure if we catch a killer, the mayor might let the ticket slide."

"I wouldn't count on it."

Screech! Miss May took a sharp left down Larkspur Road. *My goodness, were we going where I thought we were going?* "Hold on a second. What are we doing on Larkspur?"

Miss May looked over at me. "Figure it out yet?"

Then she pulled up a long driveway to a big colonial house. And I spied Florence Fitz waiting near the walkway, with two big suitcases beside her.

Miss May climbed out of the car with her arms spread and a big smile on her face. "Florence! Going on vacation?"

Florence looked up and froze. "May. Hi. Uh... Vacation?"

Miss May looked down at Florence's bulging suitcases. "That's what it looks like. Unless you start every morning off by packing two suitcases and loitering outside your own home in the freezing cold."

Florence shifted her weight from one foot to the other. "Oh. Right. The—the bags. I forgot I'm standing here with two giant bags."

Miss May nodded. "Yup. If I didn't know any better, which I do, I think. I'm not sure? Does that expression make sense to you?"

"Doesn't make sense to me," I said.

"Well anyway," Miss May continued. "If I didn't know any better, I'd say it looks like you're waiting for a ride to the airport."

Florence flashed a nervous smile. "I...uh...that's not... what are you doing here?"

In a flourish, Miss May pulled a pie out of her bag. Yet again, it surprised me that she was packing pie, and I'd had no idea. Despite the tension in the air, I had to bite my lip to keep from laughing.

Miss May handed the pie to Florence. "Chelsea and I are doing our early morning deliveries before we open up shop for the day."

Florence narrowed her eyes as she accepted the pie. "I didn't order a pie."

"I know. I felt so bad about what happened at the funeral home. This is my way of apologizing. Instead of emotionally eating, I like to emotionally feed people."

Florence stared down at the pie. "Great. Well. I forgive you, so, yeah, we're all good now."

Miss May smiled. "That is such a weight off my back, and let me tell you, I can feel my joints thanking me already. How have you been, anyway? Is there anything else I can do?"

"You can leave!" Principal Fitz's voice was sharp and angry. She cleared her throat and tried again in a calmer tone. "I'm sorry. I'm still on edge, if you must know, barely through the first stage of grief, not sure I'll ever make it to stage number two. I need to be alone, that's all, alone with my thoughts. It's hard for me to take visitors. Thanks again for the pie."

Florence shuffled us back toward the bus, then an excited voice rang out from near the front door. "Flo! Did you remember to pack the chargers?"

I turned to see Assistant Principal Marvin exiting the house, holding two beautiful leather duffel bags. Marvin froze when he saw me and Miss May on the driveway, and his excited tone disappeared. "What are you two doing here?"

Miss May retained her 'country baker,' persona, smiling wide. "Delivering a pie, that's all. What are you doing here, Marvin?"

"Uh...I was just...helping Florence grieve." Marvin took a cautious step toward us. "A bit early in the AM to deliver a pie."

"That's true," Miss May said. "We're also here to bring you in for the murders of Charles Fitzpatrick and Vlad...the bookie."

Marvin walked down from the porch. "That's not funny."

"I'm not joking," Miss May said. "And you're not laughing. Are you laughing, Chels?"

I shook my head and looked over at Florence. The woman hadn't moved an inch since our arrival. She looked so much like a statue, I half-expected a pigeon to alight and take a poop on her head.

Marvin climbed down the porch and nudged Florence, a smile still plastered on his face. "Florence is excited for our big trip, that's all. Isn't that right, Florence?"

Florence tried and failed to smile. It came out more like a lip seizure. "Yes. So excited."

"So you are taking a vacation," Miss May deadpanned.

"Where are you going?" I asked.

"Top secret," Marvin said with a wink. "And look! That must be our ride now."

A black SUV rolled up the driveway and stopped behind the bus. Marvin waved and stepped toward it, but Miss May cut him off.

"You can't go yet," Miss May said. "I haven't told you how I know you did it."

32

CONFESSIONS AND CAPTURES

"*I* didn't do anything." Marvin took another step toward the SUV, but Miss May blocked his path.

"Humor me, then," Miss May said. "I got up early and trekked all the way out here in the cold. The least you can do is listen to my stupid theory."

"We don't have time for that. Let's go Florence."

Miss May cleared her throat. "It started with you and Charles. He was smart, but you're smarter, aren't you, Marvin? You figured out that Charles was planning on running away with everyone's money long before anyone else had a clue. Then you decided you needed to earn his trust. You sold him on your technological expertise."

Marvin scoffed. "What expertise? I have to call my nephew for help whenever I want to make a social media post."

"I don't believe that for a millisecond, Marvin. I saw that computer you've got set up in the office at the school. That's professional. They don't sell those in stores."

Marvin stammered. "I—I got that as a gift. I don't know anything about it."

"Anyway," Miss May said. "You wormed your way into Charles' good graces. Then you helped him forge his bank statements and trick the cops into thinking the money was all in his business account."

This was all news to me. *How had Miss May pieced all of this together?*

She continued, "After that came the coup de grace. You convinced Charles to transfer the money into an anonymous digital currency, so the cops couldn't trace it back to him. Bonus: once he converted the cash to cryptocurrency, whoever had the password could access the money, and take it all for themselves. Charles realized you were after the funds, and he threatened to expose you to the whole town. He figured he could convince them you were the real thief and use you as a scapegoat. So you killed Charles with foxglove from Florence's porch."

"But Detective Hudson said..." I stopped myself before I said more, but I couldn't hide my confusion. *Foxglove? Wayne told us that Charles froze to death.*

Marvin charged toward the waiting SUV. "This is ridiculous. We're leaving. We have to go to JFK!"

"I'm not going to stop you, Marvin. Do you see police here? I haven't called anyone."

Marvin looked around, and so did I. Miss May was right. No cop cars. Anywhere.

Wait, what? What kind of master plan was this?

My teeth chattered in terror, but Miss May was as cool as a winter cucumber, and her voice didn't waver as she spoke.

"You thought you had gotten away with Charles' murder, didn't you, Marvin? You tricked him into meeting up with you in the woods, and you gave him just enough of the poisonous flower to slow his heart rate, which put him into a deep sleep. Then you left him there to freeze. You didn't think anyone would know about the foxglove. You thought it would look like he got drunk and wandered off."

That's cold, I thought and nearly giggled. I scolded myself for being tickled by such a bad pun at such a serious moment.

Marvin scoffed. "Sounds pretty out-there, May."

"It was a perfect plan. Except you failed to account for his gambling problem. Charles had racked up a big bill by the time he died. So Vlad came up to collect. He figured out you had the money. He located the digital key to the cryptocurrency account. And he was about to steal it all. So you stopped him with a pair of scissors to the back. Weak attempt to frame the scorned hairdresser, by the way. Why would she wrap up a pair of scissors in her own flier and toss them under a bridge?"

Florence grunted. "I told him to plant the scissors in her salon, but the little imp got scared!"

Miss May's eyes widened. So did mine. *Whoa.* Florence had come un-statued. Her stone countenance was alive and angry, like a cartoon image of the quintessential scary principal.

"And you want to know something else, May?" Florence dropped her pie and stepped closer to us. "You should be ashamed of yourself."

Miss May stared down at the ruined pie. "Wh-why?"

"Because!" Florence continued. "You completely bought my 'scared little woman' act. And you assumed that the man was the mastermind! You're just like everyone else I've encountered in my life. All the people who told me a woman could never be valedictorian. All the people who told me a woman could never be principal! You're just like my pathetic husband, who thought he could cheat on me, and steal from me, and get away with it! You underestimated me. You think I was growing a poisonous flower on my doorstep by accident? Ha! This plan has been underway for years. Yeah, Marvin helped. But I told him what to do every step of the way. Including this getaway. So if you'll excuse me. As Marvin said. We're headed to JFK."

Florence clapped at Marvin. "Get the bags!"

Marvin leapt toward the bags and gathered them up as Principal Florence Fitz strode toward the SUV.

Huh. I always knew she wasn't a good principal. This wasn't the time for I-told-you-so's, but I felt a sick sense of satisfaction knowing that my teenage self had been right to hate Principal Fitz.

Seconds later, Florence and Marvin had climbed into the waiting car, and their great escape was underway.

Miss May and I watched as the SUV rumbled down the driveway and disappeared around the bend. "What the heck was that?" I asked. "How are we just going to let them—"

"Detective Wayne Hudson please." Miss May already had her phone to her ear. "Sure. I'll hold."

She covered the receiver and turned to me. "Do you want to do the talking?"

"Uh...What would I say?"

Miss May shrugged and turned back to the phone. "Hey Wayne. You need to send a few officers over to the Pine Grove bridge immediately. The one that heads out toward the shortcut to LaGuardia."

"Not LaGuardia," I said. "JFK."

Miss May glared at me. "It's definitely LaGuardia. Yup. You were wrong about the killer. Uh-huh. I've got the whole confession recorded on my phone. OK. We'll talk later. Go cut them off at the bridge. We'll see you there."

"If you're wrong about the airport, they're going to get away!"

"I'm not wrong, Chelsea. Think about it. Why would they make such a point to mention JFK if that's really where they wanted to go?"

I shrugged. "I guess."

"Besides," Miss May said. "They were using Big Betty's Airport Shuttle, and Betty hates JFK. She'll only do LaGuardia and occasionally Newark, for some awful reason."

"So that's how you knew," I said.

Miss May pumped the gas and followed the sign toward the Pine Grove Bridge. "That plus my intuition. Yes."

Intuition. *Like my inkling that Florence was an evil principal all along.* I held my tongue, telling myself it was still too soon to gloat. But inside, I did a little I-was-right dance.

Miss May took a sharp turn and glanced at me. "You haven't complained about my driving all day," she said. "Have you noticed that? Not even when we drove to Florence's house, and I was gunning it on the way over there."

"That's true," I said. "I haven't yelped or squealed or anything, all day."

"Seems to me you're getting used to riding in cars," Miss May said. "Maybe that means you're ready to start driving one?"

I nodded. "Maybe I'll sign up for my road test tomorrow."

"That sounds like a great idea." Miss May smiled. But her smile faded as we approached the bridge. "Whoa momma!"

There were ten squad cars up ahead.

Three had blocked the entrance to the bridge. The

others encircled the SUV. They all had their lights flashing, and armed police officers crouched behind every vehicle.

Miss May skidded to a halt and jumped out of the VW bus.

I called out, "Miss May! Be careful!" But Miss May had already plowed up to the first cop car. And when she turned back and waved me toward her, I knew everything was OK.

I flopped out of the van and witnessed something I never expected to see.

The principal and assistant principal from my high school, face down and hand-cuffed, at the foot of the Pine Grove Bridge.

After Wayne stuffed Florence and Marvin into separate squad cars, he walked over to me with a coy smile.

"You and your little old aunt need to stop with this amateur sleuth racket," he said.

I smiled. "But we're so good at it. And I don't think Miss May would appreciate being called little, or old. FYI."

"I'll keep that mind," he said.

I nodded. "Please do."

Wayne met my eyes, and then, as if in slo-mo, he reached out and brushed a piece of hair off my face. I held my breath. *A hair graze! Just like in the movies! Oh my gosh, this was so incredibly, divinely romantic—*

"You've got a piece of food in your hair," Wayne said.

I hung my head and laughed. "Oh." *What do you say to that?* "Can you tell what it is?"

"Could be cheese."

I laughed. "I did resolve to eat more cheese recently."

Wayne flicked away the unidentifiable food. We looked at each other for a long moment.

"You always keep a snack in your bangs?" Wayne asked with a smug grin.

"No! Don't you have prisoners to process or something?"

"I do." Wayne said. "Don't tell anyone I told you this, especially not your aunt, but uh, good job."

"Thanks."

Wayne ambled away with big, confident strides. And thus ended the most romantic moment of my adult life. Cheese in hair or not.

Miss May approached as soon as Wayne was out of hearing distance.

"That looked like an almost kiss," she said.

"I had food in my hair."

Miss May nodded. "That's what you get for skipping the shower last night. Was it cheese?"

"So it would seem."

Miss May laughed, and so did I. Then we watched as the squad cars drove away and headed back toward town.

"Two killers on this case," Miss May said. "You think maybe next time we'll catch three?"

"I really hope there's not a next time," I said.

Miss May looked at me. "Of course. Murder is a horrible thing. And Pine Grove's had enough of it to last a lifetime." Miss May watched as the cop cars pulled away and drove back toward town. "Still. I had fun."

I grinned. "Yeah. Me too. I guess. Even though you did all the real detecting."

"Every Sherlock has a Watson," Miss May said.

"So you're Sherlock now?" I asked.

Miss May patted me on the back and didn't answer. But I

could tell by the way she smiled that she liked the comparison. I didn't hate it either.

I wonder if Watson ever had food in his hair? I thought as we walked back toward the van.

A question for another day.

33

DANCING ON THE TABLES

*T*eeny was irate when we regaled her with all the grit and glory surrounding our latest case. She felt so left out that she closed down the restaurant for a whole day, just so she could milk every single detail about the case out of me and Miss May.

At least, that's why Teeny said she was closing down the restaurant. Actually, I think she just wanted a break from making hashbrown lasagna for all her rabid fans. She even suggested taking the dish off the menu. I nearly cried when she said that, but Teeny assured me she'd still make me a special HBL sometimes. *Whew.*

Even though *Grandma's* was technically closed, half the town showed up to celebrate the arrest of Charles' killers and to hear Miss May and me recount the tale. We'd solved the biggest scandal in Pine Grove's recent history, and people were eating up the juicy drama. I suspect most people were also hoping to get a hint about the mystery that remained unsolved: *Where had all the money gone?*

Gigley arrived about halfway through the party, and when he entered, the townspeople cheered and broke into a chant. "Gig-ley! Gig-ley!" Once the citizens of Pine Grove had realized Gigley wasn't a murderer, his surly e-mails made him a hero. People hadn't stopped quoting him for days.

Gigley waved off his fans with a good-natured smile, but the chants didn't stop. Eventually, Gigley joined in. Later in the day, we managed to talk him into reading some of his Carter Communications emails out loud, and he had the whole restaurant rolling in laughter like it was a comedy club. *Fiery inferno! Hysterical!*

As the sun drooped into the west, more and more people showed up. Teeny opened one, then two, then ten bottles of wine, and what had started as a casual get together turned into a full-blown party. Missing money be damned. Pine Grove was having fun tonight.

Liz held court in one corner, recounting her crucial role in alerting to the town to Charles' misconduct. Miss May and Teeny remained in their booth, and Teeny played up her sister Peach's involvement in the case more and more each time she retold the story. Rita showed up with little sleeping Vinny (who was sporting a giant pair of noise-cancelling baby headphones), and then Brian came, and so did Gigley's secretary Deb. Familiar faces streamed in and out of *Grandma's*, including KP, Sudeer and his wife, and my sweet cousin Maggie.

Granny watched it all from behind the counter. At least, I think she watched it. She might have been asleep.

The only person who was missing from the party was Jennifer Paul. I tried not to worry about it, but I felt bad about how things had gone down on the beach. Jennifer was not my favorite person, but she also wasn't a murderer. And we had treated her like one.

That's why I was glad when I saw her slip through the

front door a little later in the night. The room got quiet when she entered. Then, she yanked a gleaming pair of scissors from her bag and yelled, "Who needs a haircut?!"

It was almost a too-soon moment, and the air sizzled with silence for a tense moment. Then the room erupted into cheers and laughter, and hands shot up in the air. Jennifer's salon being out of commission had left a lot of shaggy-haired customers wandering around Pine Grove. Jennifer looked right at me. "Chelsea? How about you? Or would you rather go back into the city?"

I hesitated. All eyes were on me. I took a deep breath and then shouted over the music, "Snip away!"

Everyone hooted and hollered in support. Moments later, I was in a chair, half-choked by one of those hair-bib-thingies, and hair was falling all around me like snow. Jennifer was about halfway done with the job when the front door swung open and Wayne stepped through the door. The room fell into a wide-eyed hush. Wayne's voice boomed into the quiet. "This party is over, people!"

This wasn't good news for anyone, especially not my hair.

"What are you talking about?" Gigley demanded in his sternest lawyer voice.

"We got a noise complaint. Sorry, everyone."

Teeny stood on a table. "Tough luck! This is my property, and I'm not done having fun yet!"

Wayne laughed. "OK, well, good to know you respect authority, Teeny." He looked around. "But you got me. I'm just joshing you. There was no complaint."

"Why are you here then?" Teeny puffed out her chest. She was feeling extra Napoleonic since she'd had a few glasses of wine.

"I'm here...with information about everyone's money," Wayne said.

A buzz swept through the room as people muttered and shouted out questions about their money.

Wayne raised his arms in the air. The crowd stilled, and Wayne continued in a grave voice. "The Pine Grove Police Department..." He looked out over the crowd and spoke with slow and deliberate poise. "Has recovered all stolen funds. You should all have your money back within the month."

There were three seconds of thick silence, then Gigley yelled at the top of his lungs, "We got our money back!"

The crowd erupted in gleeful hoorahs. Teeny and Gigley danced together on top of a table. An old woman cried and hugged her dog. Brian and Rita took a shot of whiskey. Teeny pulled Miss May onto the table, and I saw my aunt dance for maybe the second time in my life.

I hung back by the far wall, taking it all in. Wayne caught my eye from across the room. I smiled at him and ran a nervous hand through my half-cut hair. No food particles, but I hadn't looked in a mirror since Jennifer had taken her scissors to my locks. *So, fingers crossed, I guess.*

Then I felt a tickle on my feet. When I looked down, there was Petey, crawling around with a sudsy sponge, sweating as he worked.

"Petey. What are you doing down there?"

"Scrubbing baseboards," he said. "Teeny says I can't join the party until I'm done, unless I quit and go back to school."

"So then quit." I reached down and offered Petey my hand.

He grabbed it, pulled himself up, and tossed the sponge down into a disgusting bucket.

"Hey everybody!" he said.

The crowd turned and looked at Petey.

"I'm going back to school!"

Once again, the crowd erupted. But this time, they were chanting Petey's name. I laughed and climbed up on the table to dance alongside Miss May, hair-bib-thingy and all.

For one glorious moment, I felt completely carefree. The lights were dim, the music was loud, and I was dancing like no one was watching, even though everyone was watching, including Detective Wayne Hudson. I was on fire. I was unstoppable. I was also standing too close to the edge of the table.

I realized my mistake two seconds too late. The table shifted, I tumbled sideways, and I fell gracelessly onto a chair and sprained my wrist. *Oh well. At least I didn't have cheese in my hair.*

The End

Dear Readers,

Thank you for joining Chelsea, Teeny and Miss May on another fun and mysterious adventure! *Candy Apple Killer* is the next book in the Apple Orchard Series.

You'll love this cozy because everyone loves plucky detectives who solve mysteries with a smile!

Search *Candy Apple Killer* on Amazon to grab your copy today.

Chelsea

P.S. Want a free cozy mystery *plus* a free cozy cookbook? Join the Chelsea Thomas Reader Club!

www.chelseathomasauthor.com

Printed in Great Britain
by Amazon